RELAX

RELAX

*How You Can Feel Better, Reduce Stress,
and Overcome Tension*

EDITED BY JOHN WHITE
AND JAMES FADIMAN

Produced by Richard Gallen

The Confucian Press

Published by
THE CONFUCIAN PRESS, INC.

Copyright © 1976 by
The Confucian Press, Inc.
Printed in the United States of America
First Printing—February 1976
Second Printing—April 1976

ACKNOWLEDGMENTS

"Shaking," "Differential Relaxation," "Learning to Recognize Tension" and "Letting Movement Happen" are from *An Everyday Guide to Your Health* by David Stuart Sobel and Faith Louise Hornbacher. Copright © 1973 by David Stuart Sobel and Faith Louise Hornbacher. Reprinted by permission of Grossman Publishers, a division of The Viking Press, Inc.

"Relax Your Face" is reprinted by permission from *Go to Health* by Communications Research Machines, Inc. Copyright © 1972 by Communications Research Machines, Inc. and published by Delacorte Press.

The selection from *Ten Ways to Meditate* by Paul Reps was published by John Weatherhill, Inc. and is reprinted by permission

"The Relief is Worth the Effort" is from *Ten Days Journey Into the Self* by Shree Gurudev Chitrabhanu (Munishri Chitrabhanu), and is reprinted by permission of the Jain Meditation International Center, New York.

The selection from *The Zen of Running* by Fred Rohé is reprinted by permission of Random House, Inc. and The Bookworks Copyright © 1974 by Fred Rohé.

The selection from *Sense Relaxation Below Your Mind* by Bernard Gunther is reprinted by permission of Macmillan Publishing Co., Inc. Copyright © 1968 by Bernard Gunther.

"Stress Who Needs It?" is reprinted from *Stress Without Distress* by Hans Selye, M.D. Copyright © 1974 by Hans Selye, M.D. Reprinted by permission of J. B. Lippincott Company.

"What to Do When You're Under Stress" was reprinted from *U.S. News & World Report.*

"Your Innate Asset for Combating Stress" by Herbert Benson is reprinted by permission from *Harvard Business Review*, July-August 1974. Copyright © 1974 by the President and Fellows of Harvard College. All rights reserved.

"The Relaxation Response" by Herbert Benson et al. is reprinted from *Psychiatry*, Vol. 37, 1974, pages 37-46 by special permission of The William Alanson White Psychiatric Founda-

CONTENTS

INTRODUCTION

"Relax."

It's a magical word—the key to reducing tension, anxiety, nervousness, stress.

And these states *should* be reduced, because being chronically "uptight" leads to all sorts of physical and psychological disabilities. They lead from stress to distress —to bodily pain and mental suffering.

Stress is a disease that creates other diseases, according to psychiatrist Ainsley Meares in *Relief Without Drugs*. First it affects, he says, and then it *in*fects. Similarly, *Fortune* magazine (May 1973) reports that manifestations of chronic mental and emotional stress have long since replaced epidemics of infectious diseases as medical problems in the rich nations. Stress sickness, the article notes, is a byproduct of the industrial age—the general scourge of health in advanced societies.

Just look at some of the problems for which relaxation is a major element in their cure: insomnia, peptic ulcer, nervous fatigue, migraine headache, nail biting, depression, stuttering, constipation, asthma, high blood pressure, acute dermatitis, arthritis, painful menstrual periods, premature ejaculation, frigidity, and sterility. Some authorities would add alcoholism and attempted suicide.

Folk wisdom has long recognized relaxation as a proper prescription for much of what ails us. It doesn't take a doctor to tell you that a vacation at the ocean or in the mountains can do wonders to lift your spirit. Just "getting away from it all" for a day's fishing or hiking is powerfully refreshing. Sports of all kinds are also a frequently sought remedy for relief from the pressures of the day. So are music, painting, and other hobbies. A cup of hot tea or coffee after a meal—and even a rocking chair—likewise seem to melt away tension. A less wise means, though widely used, is the five-o'clock martini or beer after work. Almost as prevalent, and even more unwise, is the use of drugs, especially tranquilizers. Through these and other means, most people learn how to "cope."

Coping goes only so far, however, and beyond that we pay a heavy price for not facing stressful situations honestly. Anxiety creeps upon us, interfering with living and inhibiting performance, efficiency, and even learning. Dr. Zoe Lasker of Boston University observed in an unpublished study of the effects of transcendental meditation for anxiety, drug abuse, cigarette smoking, and alcohol consumption that excessive anxiety seems to be a primary source of ineffective coping and functioning. "In appropriate circumstances," she wrote,

> arousal [of the nervous system] to a lesser extent than excessive anxiety can provide important information to the organism; it is necessary for survival to warn the organism of impending danger. Arousal based on real dangers in the external world is considered by Freud to be "reality anxiety." Arousal that is not based on an objective appraisal of the external world but rather springs from imagined threats is considered neurotic anxiety. Excessive anxiety reduces the efficiency of the individual in satisfying his needs, disturbs interpersonal relations, and produces confusion in thinking. Severe anxiety conveys no useful information to the person; instead it produces confusion and impedes performance.*

Medical science learned earlier this century that the body has a "flight-or-fight" response which prepares it for resistance to threatening situations. This is the "wisdom of the body" placed in us through billions of years of evolution.

Nature's wisdom, however, is not always the controlling factor in human society (although it should be). Often this "useful physiologic feature of survival," as Harvard cardiologist Dr. Herbert Benson terms it, produces its proper response in situations where human society has declared that fighting or running is unacceptable or inappropriate.

*Available from Students International Meditation Society, 1015 Gayley Avenue, Los Angeles, California 90028.

Whether the situation is at school, where a child is faced with bad grades, or at the office, where a worker feels that his boss is "climbing all over my back," or at home, where a mother feels that her children are tying her down to a career in housekeeping, the result is varying degrees of rage or fear.

But custom, tradition, law, and other forms of subtle coercion usually keep us from expressing those emotions and from working off the bodily responses occurring along with them: the increased blood pressure, the extra adrenalin in the system, the tightness in the gut and throat. Why? "It's bad manners." "Well, my dear, we simply don't do that here." "Watch it, mac—you're gettin' outta line!"

The results are health-wrecking. And the proportions of that human wreckage are growing enormously.

The wisdom of the body goes deep, however. The body has an innate impulse for health and wholeness, and nature won't be kept down for long. Suppressed feelings and ignored tensions come out in a wide variety of ways, calling our attention to these unresolved problem areas.

These signals can be used to restore health. Dr. Theodore Rubin, in his article "Peace Without Pills" (*Ladies Home Journal*, November 1974), put it this way:

> Tension and anxiety—the very opposites of inner peace—often lead to inner peace if we don't tranquilize these feelings away [through drugs]. This sounds contradictory, but it isn't. Anxiety is often a signal that something is going on within us which we haven't faced, but which is attempting to surface. Allowing real feelings, desires and ideas to surface not only results in growth of aliveness, but also permits us the peace that is lost when we try to repress aspects of ourselves.

These remarks are indicative of a trend among health authorities, therapists, and the general public, who are coming to recognize that illness, disability, and stress can play a creative role in personal growth.

One of the key elements employed by this movement is another of the body's useful features for survival. Again we use Dr. Benson's term for it: the "relaxation response." He defines it as an integrated physiologic response that appears to counteract the harmful effects of stress. Dr. Benson explains the matter in his best-selling book, *The Relaxation Response*, and in his article reprinted here, "Your Innate Asset for Combating Stress." We are grateful to him for allowing us to use it and another article, "The Relaxation Response," which deals in depth with the physiology of stress We are also grateful to him for his thoughtful comments during this book's preparation.

Why is it so hard to relax? Babies can relax anywhere, any time. You can see them sleeping papooselike in a portable seat on Father's back or curled around Mother's shoulder. It makes no difference whether they're at home or on a crowded, noisy bus. Wherever they are, they're relaxed and comfortable.

Could *you* sleep that way? Could you even *relax* that way? Probably not.

But why not? How is it that babies—small, helpless infants—can do so easily what most adults cannot? The answer has many levels to it. Included are unconscious learned reactions that produce chronic tenseness in the muscles. Also included are subtle conditioned psychological responses that evoke an image of oneself. Dr Marjorie Raskin of the Langley Porter Neuropsychiatric Institute in San Francisco spoke of the problem in the previously mentioned *Fortune* article:

> Everyone can cope with a little anxiety, but the person who becomes afraid to do something because he thinks he can't control himself is the person I'm studying. And that represents about 5 percent of the population. Their fear of failure becomes haunting, and patients become homebound. Headaches are frequent. Insomnia is almost inevitable. Chronic anxiety does not shorten your life. But people who have high intelligence quotients—and most anxiety victims do— don't live up to their potential. Their ability to produce is killed.

Dr. Raskin's remarks touch on the matter of self-image as the key to relaxing. This is where we can begin to see beyond the surface into deeper layers. And when we get to the bottom, we find that most relaxation-related problems can be understood as symptoms of a single underlying cause: ego.

What is ego? It is our sense of self, our "I." It is an idealized self-image that we carry around mentally and try to project onto others. But the interesting thing about ego is that *it doesn't exist!* Certainly it's not physical or material in any way. It's only a picture of ourselves that we keep in the forefront of our minds as we think and act. But even that mental picture isn't really true, because our actual self is in many ways quite different and quite greater than the ego image we construct—*and we know it!*

Ego is an illusion, then—a great big lie that we tell to ourselves. Yet how much of our lives it governs! When Ego is the name of the game, everything has to be done protect it, to keep the image bright and shiny. We have to say the right things in order to impress others or to hide our true feelings. We have to dress in certain ways that are called "fashionable" in order to show that we're sophisticated. We have to gain status through cars and college degrees and by staying at the "right" hotels and reading the "right" books. What it amounts to is a lot of unnecessary bother—tension, stress, anxiety, tightness—in an attempt to be something that we know isn't truly us.

Animals never have relaxation-related problems, for the simple reason that they don't have a self-image. Neither do babies. This is the answer to our question about why babies can be so relaxed: they haven't developed an ego that keeps them constantly on guard and uptight. A comment by meditation researcher Durand Kiefer on this subject is especially important:

> The core of all human suffering (as distinguished from pain) is the uniquely human sense of self that we call selfconsciousness or egocentricity. Every action or event in human experience which effectively decreases or eliminates selfconsciousness decreases human suffering proportionately, and every action or event in human experience which effectively increases selfconsciousness increases human suffering proportionately. . . .
>
> Infants generally display no selfconsciousness, and hence no nervousness, and almost all contemporary

attacks upon selfconsciousness, either mystical or psychological, are directly regressive in their effect. . . . Almost universally, they promote infantile spontaneity, or neural relaxation [relaxation of the nervous system], a first step toward infantile unselfconsciousness.

Here we are dealing with the root level of suffering and relaxation-related problems. Self-knowledge—that is, knowledge of our true self in all its potential for health and wholeness—is the first step toward cure. It is the means whereby we can leap that first hurdle of feeling that nothing can be done.

Much can be done, because, as Dr. Elmer Green of the Menninger Clinic points out, human beings have a remarkable capacity to control the nervous system. This is precisely what happened in the first place to cause our stress. We learned to tense certain muscles; we learned to set up certain signals firing through the nerve circuits. *But we learned it unconsciously*. Amazing. isn't it, that we can be so skilled in control of our bodies without knowing it?

This book is intended to show you how to make the unconscious conscious. You are always in control, whether or not you're conscious of it. But, to relieve tension, you must become aware of the mechanisms and influences that have set up the stress response in the first place. You must bring the process within your field of awareness. In that way you will learn *consciously* to modify the experience of your nervous system through an act of mind. You will be replacing the ego's unconscious control of your body with some degree of enlightened self-awareness that can simply tell the body, "Stop it!" With practice, the near-perfect ease and relaxation of a baby can be yours.

The methods and information surveyed here are natural ways of dealing with anxiety by evoking the relaxation response. By no means is this book comprehensive. Rather, we have attempted to present a sample representation of the most effective procedures and therapies for promoting physical and mental well-being through relaxation. Some require a teacher or therapist; others can be self-administered. Some are useful means of intervention for specific problems; others can be better understood as general preventive therapy. All aim at diminishing human stress and promoting growth, health, and constructive change.

We'll begin with some "quickies" to loosen us up physically and put us in the right frame of mind. Then we'll have an interview with an authority in the field of stress to see how we're doing.

—J.W. AND J.F.

I
WARM-UP EXERCISES

In walking, just walk.
In sitting, just sit.
Above all, don't wobble.

—*Chinese Proverb*

SHAKING

DAVID STUART SOBEL

A quick way of draining off excess tension and relaxing tight muscles is shaking. With your arms hanging loosely at your sides, begin by shaking your hands. Then let the vigorous vibration move up to include your arms and then your shoulders. Feel both arms vibrate energetically and rapidly. Then let the shaking slowly subside and feel the tingling throughout your body. Now loosely shake one leg—then the other.

From *To Your Health*.

RELAX YOUR FACE

Most of us are totally unaware that our facial area—forehead, eyes, lips, tongue, jaw, and so on—gets tense, and because we are often judged and responded to by our facial expressions, it is important to know how to look relaxed. Before doing the facial exercises, go to a mirror and try to assume your normal facial expression—study it.

Now settle back comfortably in a chair or on the floor. Let your muscles go limp. Wrinkle your forehead tighter and tighter. Now relax and smooth it out. Picture your scalp and forehead smooth. Now frown. Study the tension. Relax. Close your eyes as tightly as you can. Notice the tension. Relax your eyes, keeping them closed. Feel the relaxation. Now clench your teeth together and press your tongue hard against the roof of your mouth. Feel the tension. Now relax, letting your lips part slightly; relax the muscles of your tongue.

As you relax more and more feel the tension dissipate from your forehead and scalp, eyes, jaws, lips, tongue, and throat. Now return to the mirror—do you look as relaxed as you feel?

From *Go to Health* (Communications Research Machines, Inc.).

From *Ten Ways to Meditate*.

PAUL REPS

when moving
do not disturb
the breath

move with it
smooth
even

each evening
silently
observe
any thought
any feel

so simple
delightful
very peaceful too

THE RELIEF IS WORTH THE EFFORT

MUNISHRI CHITRABHANU

Once your President Lincoln was returning to the White House, riding in his carriage and dressed in his best, when he noticed a small pig by the side of the road, mired in mud. It was squealing and squirming wildly, but all its efforts merely drove it deeper into the mud. Lincoln ordered the coach to stop, got out, and waded into the mire. He tugged and pulled until he managed to free the pig. Upon his arrival home, his family and friends noticed the mud all over his clothes, and while he went to change them, the coachman explained what had happened. When the President reappeared, everyone flocked around him, praising him for his kindness. He told them, "Please save your praises. When I saw this little creature in such distress, it was as if there were a thorn driven into my own heart. And so I plucked it out. Therefore it was really my own pain that I eased more than that of the pig."

From *Ten Days Journey into the Self.*

LEARNING TO RECOGNIZE TENSION

DAVID STUART SOBEL

Lie down flat on your back with eyes closed and arms resting limply by your sides. Begin by bending your left hand back at the wrist (not bending at the elbow). While holding this position steadily for several minutes, notice the faint sensation in the upper portion of your left forearm—not the strong, easier-to-recognize strain at the wrist or hand, but the duller, more diffuse sensation in the upper forearm. This sensation is the mark of muscle tension. It accompanies all effort and activity. Compare this sensation with the feeling in your relaxed right forearm. Become thoroughly acquainted with the sensation of tension so that you can recognize it whenever it occurs in any part of your body.

To relax, simply go limp and let your hand fall by its own weight. Notice how the sensation of tenseness in your forearm diminishes when you let go completely. The absence of tension, the absence of effort is relaxation. Remember, relaxation requires no effort; in fact, any effort to relax (by shifting your arm or engaging muscles anywhere) actually causes tension. So don't try to relax. Just stop bending your hand back, stop doing, and let relaxation happen. Try bending your hand back several times more, holding it for a few moments, and then releasing it. Explore the differences between the sensations of muscle tension and muscle relaxation, between doing and not-doing, between effort and no-effort.

Practice this method of tensing and relaxing each muscle group in your body: opening and closing your jaws, hunching and letting down your shoulders, knitting and smoothing your forehead, lifting and letting your feet down, and so on.

From *To Your Health.*

From *THE ZEN OF RUNNING.*

FRED ROHÉ

don't overdo it.
underdo it.
you aren't running because
you're in a hurry to get somewhere

you will be able to run tirelessly
if you follow this simple rule:
Run *within* your breath,

do not run *ahead* of your breath.
(you have to run
to discover what that means.)

From *SENSE RELAXATION BELOW YOUR MIND.*

BERNARD GUNTHER

after reading
the following instructions
take your time
and carry them out.

Sit straight, not rigid
in a chair.
Close your eyes
and follow your thoughts
for 1 minute.
Then let the words go and
become aware of how you feel,
not how you think you feel
or how you'd like to feel
but your actual feelings
and sensations as they are
in the next minute.
Now shift your attention
to your feet and
without moving them in any way
become conscious of what they
are resting on.
Then take 15–20 seconds
to feel-experience
(rather than think or imagine)
the following areas
of your body:
your feet, each of your toes
(without moving them),
the top of your feet, your ankles,
calves, knees, thighs,

buttocks, the chair
that is supporting you;
your stomach, chest, back,
the back of the chair;
your shoulders, arms, elbows,
forearms, wrists, hands,
each of the fingers;
your neck, lips, cheeks,
nose, eyes, face;
forehead, top of the head,
back of your head:
your entire body.
Experience your breathing,
the sounds in the room
and how you feel right now
and then slowly open your eyes.
Now with your eyes open,
bend your fingers at the joints
and begin tapping
the top of your head:
a lively half-inch bouncing
vigorous tap like rain falling
(tap 15–20 seconds in each area).
Next tap around the ears and
the sides of the head.
Then over the forehead.
Now re-tap over your entire head,
doing an especially good job
over any place that feels
like it needs a little extra;
gradually let the tapping
subside. Put your hands down
to your sides, close your eyes
and become aware
of how your head feels
as a result
of what you've just done
and then slowly
open your eyes.
Now close your eyes
and slowly
bring your hands
towards your face;

the heels of your hands
come to rest on the cheeks,
the palms cover the eyes,
the fingers rest
over the forehead.

Stay with your eyes covered
for 1 minute;
be sensitive to your eyes
and the inside of your head;
feel how things are there;
without creating any changes,
just allow
whatever wants to occur.
Slowly take your hands away,
experience how you feel,
and open your eyes.

STRESS—WHO NEEDS IT?

HANS SELYE

(Hans Selye, M.D., is widely regarded as the foremost investigator in the field of stress research. His work is primarily responsible for bringing the effects of stress to public attention. *Editors*.)

Stress is not something to be avoided. In fact, it . . . cannot be avoided.

In common parlance, when we say someone is "under stress," we actually mean under excessive stress or distress, just as the statement "he is running a temperature" refers to an abnormally high temperature, that is, fever. Some heat production is essential to life.

Similarly, no matter what you do or what happens to you, there arises a demand for the necessary energy required to maintain life, to resist aggression and to adapt to constantly changing external influences. Even while fully relaxed and asleep, you are under some stress. Your heart must continue to pump blood, your intestines to digest last night's dinner, and your muscles to move your chest for respiration. Even your brain is not at rest while you are dreaming.

From *Stress Without Distress*

WHAT TO DO WHEN YOU'RE UNDER STRESS*

AARON T. BECK

(Aaron T. Beck, M.D., is a psychiatrist at the University of Pennsylvania Medical School. This interview is reprinted from the September 24, 1973, issue of *U.S. News & World Report. Editors.*)

Q. Dr. Beck, is stress becoming a big problem in today's world?

A. First, let me say that it's a world in which we are very conscious of things that produce stress: the competitive pressure on executives, the upsets caused by mobility, the difficulties of modern marriage, and so on. We also see evidence that many young people are less able or less willing than before to cope with adversities.

There are no precise figures on the incidence of serious depression or severe anxiety in the United States. In my book, *Depression: Causes and Treatment*, I reviewed the statistics. There are indications that severe depression or anxiety could involve 20 per cent of the population at one point or another in their lives.

But stress itself is an old problem. At any time in the past, a great deal was said about "these harsh and perilous times" when people were believed to be undergoing more pressures than ever before. A century ago, during the Centennial celebration, Americans also worried about crime, racial problems, corruption and economic crises.

Q. Have the effects of stress changed much since then?

A. I don't think so. A century ago, such problems as depression and suicidal tendencies were diagnosed and treated.

Q. Just what is the medical definition of stress?

A. The word itself was borrowed from physics and engineering, where it has a very precise meaning: a force of sufficient magnitude to distort or deform when applied to a system.

In emotional or mental problems, it has become a "wastebasket" definition applied after the event. For instance, if we have student unrest or an increased suicide rate, the phenomenon is first observed and then the cause is generally put under the term "stress"—which can be as broad as economic instability or as highly specific as being rejected by a girl friend or boy friend. Stress can generate symptoms of depression or anxiety, or both. These disturbances can be triggered by a sense of loss—a loved one, a job, or familiar surroundings—or a sense of threat.

Q. Is there any particular period in a person's life that can be regarded as most stressful?

A. At one time I used to believe that childhood produced the most stress. Actually, it now seems clear that each period has its own set of stresses.

Q. Starting out with childhood, what are they?

A. In early life, the child has to confront and cope with two major problems:

One is the immediate family group—how to deal with any harmful elements that might be present, such as hostile parents or overly competitive brothers and sisters.

Once the child enters school, he encounters new stresses —not only the demands of school itself, but adjusting to the personality of the teacher and to the other children. These can be very stressful. Take clique formation, which I think has been very much underestimated. You find the youngster who for no apparent reason is a social isolate, and thereby his mind is stamped with the idea of being inferior to the other children, even if the home is providing all the tender loving care that parents can give. The child may go on for years feeling totally "out of it," and parents have no idea of what is wrong.

In later adolescence comes the problem of boy-girl relationships, which can be very traumatic to either sex. Perhaps this happens less so now than years ago because there seem to be fewer barriers between the sexes. I still see the problem clinically, however.

Then there are the worries over career choice and, of course, the academic stresses. In the college years, those who leave home have the strain of adjusting to a completely new set of circumstances—away from the "umbrella" of parents. After college, for most there are the problems of the first years of marriage. These can be quite serious and often lead to early divorces. The problems of having children bear more heavily on the woman, while the man has his early career problems.

Q. Do career problems remain pretty much the same until retirement?

A. No. I classify them into early, middle and late career stresses.

Q. How do the symptoms differ in each phase?

A. The actual symptoms may be the same, irrespective of the external stress factor. People seem to have a particular way of reacting to problems—obsessions, anxiety, alcohol, or whatever.

Q. Ulcers, too?

A. Yes, ulcers are a symptom that can develop at any stage. We even see them in children. But the typical ulcer personality is probably in the middle executive level, where the individual not only has external job pressures but— what is more important—the internal pressures to get ahead.

You have to understand that a good deal of what we call stress is probably internally generated. External circumstances galvanize the individual into doing and feeling things that really work against himself.

The executive-ulcer type is a person who is driving himself all the time to do his job well. But as soon as he reaches one level of success, he raises his level of aspiration higher, so there is never any letup. He tends to be a constant worrier: He fears that he is going to make a mistake or fail, or he'll worry about his subordinates. At this stage of his career he is in a constant state of turmoil.

Q. Does this produce home stresses, too?

A. Yes. It sets up all kinds of currents at home. At the minimum, he tends to neglect his family. At the maximum, he may take out all of his tensions on his wife and children.

sure that he's the only one who has gone through it, that there is nothing he can do about it, that the loneliness will last forever, and—in the case of the suicidal person—that there seems to be no alternative to ending his life.

Well, if such a person gets through his first bout of real loneliness on his own, he learns that it is not such a unique and terrible thing. Later, if another attack of loneliness comes along, the memory of having had it before and learning that eventually it disappears tends to become a coping mechanism. He learns not to indulge in misinterpretations that aggravated his feeling of loneliness.

Q. Can a middle-bracket executive learn to cope with the frustration in not getting ahead as fast as he wants to?

A. His trouble is an outgrowth of the overemphasis on achievement and the notion that a person's self-worth is dependent on how much he achieves. At its ultimate, achieving becomes a life-or-death matter to him, and he is constantly generating anxiety, just as though the ax is ready to fall at any moment.

If he can develop a more healthy attitude about achievement—learn from experience that it's a nice thing to have, but an optional extra and not an essential for existence or self-worth—then he is less likely to feel the stress of striving for a goal.

Q. What if he doesn't learn from experience?

A. He'd have to get some advice from someone who knows his problem.

Q. What are some of the ways of coping that you might advise him to consider?

A. Well, business firms and industries are conscious of this, and they have industrial psychologists who lecture and counsel individuals. I think they would tell the "uptight" executive the same thing I would—that he is trying too hard, that in fact he is more likely to get what he wants if he doesn't make the goal so important in his life.

The next thing I would recommend would be a variety of recreational pursuits. Depending on his social class and income, it would be bowling, playing tennis, gardening, going on vacations and so on. This tends to balance out his life and give him more perspective.

The problem in all these cases of stress is that the individual really loses objectivity and perspective about his or her situation. Often just talking to a psychiatrist or a counselor or a minister allows such a person to look at things from a distance and see things in broader perspective—to become less of a slave to inner drives and develop coping mechanisms.

Q. How easily can signs of troublesome stress be detected?

A. It differs for two kinds of people—the "sensitizers" and the "repressors."

The sensitizers are people who are already overly sensitive to signs of inner tension. They're very much aware of any changes in their physiology—heartburn, trouble with the gastrointestinal system, lower-back pain, headaches and so on. This awareness aggravates their troubles. Those individuals don't need to know any more than they already do about signs of tension.

The repressors are individuals who tend to be relatively oblivious of being "uptight." A friend of mine was like this. He was always wound up, and was never aware of it —though I knew about it, and so did his wife. One day he learned that he had a bleeding ulcer. Then, for the first time, we were able to move in and show him how he was living his life in such a way that getting an ulcer was inevitable. He was driving himself all the time.

In the case of the repressor, people around him have to let him know that he's drinking too much or not getting enough sleep. Overdrinking is, of course, a sign of tension. So are sleeplessness, difficulty in relating to other people, and inability to enjoy activities that brought pleasure before.

Q. How easily can symptoms be tied to a particular cause of stress?

A. In a small proportion of cases, the stress is overwhelming and very easily identifiable. Any lay person could see the connection between depression and its cause in a case where there has been the loss of a child or the breakup of a marriage.

These events have specific meanings to the individual, and it's the meaning itself that is a psychological stress. Dr. Thomas H. Holmes and his colleagues at the University of Washington have developed a "life-events scale" which is designed to measure these kinds of psychological stresses resulting from changes in life circumstances.

This scale shows that people who have become depressed

HOW DIFFERENT EVENTS CAUSE STRESS

Dr. Thomas H. Holmes, a psychiatrist, and his colleagues at the University of Washington School of Medicine in Seattle have developed a "life-events scale" designed to measure the psychological stress that can be caused by various changes in life circumstances.

The scale, Dr. Beck points out in the accompanying interview, provides a "reasonably good correlation" between life changes and onset of depression and medical problems.

Studies by Dr. Holmes indicate that an accumulation of 200 or more "life-change units" in a single year may be more disruption than an individual can withstand—and make him vulnerable to illness.

Event	Scale of Impact	Event	Scale of Impact
Death of spouse	100	Change in responsibilities at work	29
Divorce	73	Son or daughter leaving home	29
Marital separation	65	Trouble with in-laws	29
Jail term	63	Outstanding personal achievement	28
Death of close family member	63	Wife begins or stops work	26
Personal injury or illness	53	Begin or end school	26
Marriage	50	Change in living conditions	25
Fired at work	47	Revision of personal habits	24
Marital reconciliation	45	Trouble with boss	23
Retirement	45	Change in work hours or conditions	20
Change in health of family member	44	Change in residence	20
Pregnancy	40	Change in schools	20
Sex difficulties	39	Change in recreation	19
Gain of new family member	39	Change in church activities	19
Business readjustment	39	Change in social activities	18
Change in financial state	38	Mortgage or loan less than $10,000	17
Death of close friend	37	Change in sleeping habits	16
Change to different line of work	36	Change in number of family get-togethers	15
Change in number of arguments with spouse	35	Change in eating habits	15
Mortgage over $10,000	31	Vacation	13
Foreclosure of mortgage or loan	30	Christmas	12
		Minor violation of the law	11

have an unusual number of so-called "exits" from their lives—important people have left, there has been a disruption in some kind of relationship—or the loss may be an abstract possession, as in the loss of a job. It's not a perfect scale, but it's the only one I know of that has been tested. It shows reasonably good correlation of such events not only with depression but with such things as minor medical problems. I don't think it has been shown to be related to major medical diseases or to very serious psychiatric disorders such as schizophrenia.

Loss is one of the two major types of stresses that we see in psychiatric practice. In addition to losses such as jobs, it can cover a loss of self-esteem that comes when a person's level of aspiration is impossibly high.

The other major category is what I call threat—to the individual's status, goals, health, security. It's the wife who is afraid that her husband is going to run off with another woman, the student who feels he or she can't succeed academically, the executive in constant fear of losing his job.

Q. Do these categories apply to all classes of people?

A. Class doesn't make any difference. The lower-income people and students I see in the clinic have the same kinds of problems as the "main line" people I see in the suburbs.

Q. Where a specific external factor triggers the stress, can it be identified and handled with relative ease?

A. Not always. Some external situations develop slowly and are discernible only when something brings them into the open.

I can give you an example: a woman who was depressed because she felt her husband wasn't giving her as much affection as previously. In fact, she suspected he might be unfaithful to her. I talked to the husband, and he denied this, saying he was giving her as much affection as always. She continued to be depressed, and I wasn't able to get very far with her.

Then one day she discovered that he had, indeed, been unfaithful to her for quite a period of time and that her perception had been correct. Once she established this and they "had it out," she was able to cope with the problem, I was able to help her much more effectively, and within a few weeks she was over the depression.

By the way, he broke up with the girl—decided that he'd remain faithful to his wife. And that was the last time she was ever depressed.

Q. Are tranquilizers useful in handling stress?

A. They make a person feel better and may help him cope, because once he's feeling better he can plunge into the situation. They don't really teach him anything. Ideally,

I prefer to see people learn how to handle problems on their own.

Q. What about a drink for relaxation?

A. Alcoholism has become a major problem. Once a drink is advocated as a means of relaxation, it opens the door for two drinks and more. I think that the mental-health profession has targeted alcoholism as really the No. 1 addictive problem—far greater than drugs.

Q. Isn't alcoholism itself sometimes an offshoot of stress?

A. Oh, yes. You have stress, then tension, and then the alcohol to relieve tension, in the initial stages. Then you get into a vicious cycle where the alcohol itself produces undesirable effects, and the person starts drinking more to undo the undesirable effects.

Q. Is an alcoholic likelier to incur depression or anxiety?

A. One of the undesirable effects of alcoholism is depression. And alcoholism is definitely a precursor to about 20 per cent of completed suicides.

Q. What can family or friends do to help find the cause of depression or anxiety? Can a person diagnose his own problem successfully?

A. First of all, I don't want to leave out the family doctors. We do try to train our medical students to detect causes of anxiety or depression, and we also try to train family doctors to detect signs of stress in routine physical checkups or on office visits of patients with minor symptoms.

The problem with going to friends and family is that you can get either good or bad advice. It would take a massive program of public education to train laymen to know what constitutes good advice.

An individual himself may know in a sense what good advice is, but he can't give it to himself. That's why psychiatrists go to other psychiatrists for help.

Q. Which is the more common symptom—depression or anxiety?

A. Anxiety seems to be somewhat more prevalent, though it's only recently that we've been able to get some facts on this.

I developed a depression inventory that was administered to patients at a large health-maintenance organization. On routine examinations, without using the inventory, physicians ascertained that somewhere in the neighborhood of 6 to 8 per cent of the patients who came to them either for routine examination or for some mild ailment showed some depression.

However, when these patients were examined by a psychiatrist or were given the inventory, the proportion who showed at least mild degrees of depression ran as high as 12 to 15 per cent.

The impression is that anxiety runs higher, but a similar study on the prevalence of anxiety hasn't really been done. It has been estimated that at any one time at least 8 per cent of the population has symptoms of anxiety.

Q. Can a person suffer alternately from anxiety and depression?

A. They can alternate, and they can coexist. But the more severely depressed a person becomes, the less the anxiety manifests itself. In a sense, depression is a much more serious and malignant syndrome—if it progresses to the ultimate—than anxiety is.

Q. Why is that?

A. I can only speculate—that people who are anxious haven't given up. They try to do things to help themselves. Their friends will notice that they're anxious and will try to calm them down. A variety of medical aids are available to the person who is anxious. Often he or she will go to the doctor and get reassurance or medication that helps.

Depression tends to be much more subtle. It is missed in a very high proportion of cases. That study in the health-maintenance organization missed about half of the depressives—perhaps more. Therefore, depression has a greater chance of reaching an advanced stage without the individual's being aware of it or getting treatment. He's aware that something is wrong, but he'll blame it on some physical ailment or his life circumstances. He won't realize that something bad is going on inside him.

As I've mentioned before, the depressed person tends to give up. He thinks that nothing will work, that he's a failure, that nothing good can come of life. Therefore, he doesn't seek diversions the way an anxious person might. Having given up, he is much more likely to commit suicide, whereas the suicide rate among anxiety patients without depression is practically zero.

Q. Do depression and anxiety tend to develop and diminish along similar lines?

A. Anxiety, much more than depression, tends to be related to external situations. When the external situations improve, then the anxiety goes away.

Depression, on the other hand, tends to be more autonomous. Once triggered, it usually runs a relentless course. The person goes down, down, down, then bottoms out, and finally gets better. It doesn't matter if the triggering agent is no longer present—depression runs its course. Why that is, we don't know.

Q. Does the pace of modern living—the turmoil, noise, overcrowding—trigger more anxieties and depressions than a simpler existence would?

A. It's a purely speculative question. There is evidence that some individuals really benefit from modern living. When my son is in a bad mood, he turns his hi-fi set way up and becomes very relaxed. However, the decibel level deafens me.

Q. What about broad social or economic conditions? Do they lower or raise the extent of stress?

A. It seems that in rural areas, where there is a very low density of people and noise, the rate of neurosis is just as high. That is one of the reasons why I go back to the point that it is in a person's immediate situation—family, social or job—that you find the critical factors in becoming depressed or anxious.

Q. It's sometimes said that people's values and ideals are upset today, which bewilders many of them so they can't cope, and become depressed. Is that true?

A. Well, social institutions provide structures that help individuals absorb a lot of the shocks. Those who do not have these institutions may turn to something else—communes, a new religion, or something else. The people most susceptible to disorientation are those who are caught between the culture and counterculture—who have no institution at all and no sense of identity.

And I have to add that increasing mobility seems to heighten social disorientation.

Q. What can parents do to provide children with better defenses against depression and anxiety in later years?

A. At one time, children were thought of as being miniature adults—disciplined and trained to behave as adults. Then came a swing toward a much more permissive attitude, and right now we're probably in an overprotective, overpermissive phase.

My own attitude is that while it's good to give the child lots of love, it's not enough. Many kids can grow up straight and strong without getting more than the minimal daily requirement of love. What they do need is the opportunity to confront various problems when they're young and learn to cope with them.

The parents, by intervening prematurely, may prevent the child from developing within himself the tolerance for problems or acquiring problem-solving mechanisms.

Q. Isn't there the danger that exposing a youngster too early and too suddenly to stress may shatter his self-confidence?

A. Yes, that can happen. The parent should intervene when the youngster is obviously floundering and can't cope with the situation.

But the type of intervention is important. The parent shouldn't do all the coping for the child. The idea is to make it a learning experience so the child will be able to solve similar types of problems that arise later on.

Q. Suppose a family member is under stress that he or she may not be aware of, but others can see. What is the next step? Is it to get that person to a psychiatrist?

A. No. First of all, a large number of vague symptoms may really be due to a medical disorder. For example, anemia can produce symptoms very similar to those of anxiety neurosis—a person is weak, faints, and so forth.

Getting a good medical examination is always a standard procedure and it gives the patient a chance to tell the doctor about his inner worries or feelings. Many times the doctor can give general words of advice to be implemented by the patient himself or through help from friends or other persons, such as a clergyman.

It's only the more difficult cases—the ones that don't respond at that level—that should get psychiatric attention.

II

THE RELAXATION RESPONSE

I shall be able to rest one minute after I die.

—PIUS XII, *to physicians who asked
him to reduce his workload*

The title of this section comes from the second article reprinted here. Together with the first article, this section presents the essence of the best-selling book *The Relaxation Response*.

The author, Dr. Herbert Benson, is a cardiologist specializing in hypertension. He is an associate professor of medicine at Harvard Medical School and director of the Hypertension Section of Beth Israel Hospital in Boston. He has held many other positions as well, including consultant to the National Institute of Mental Health and the President's Special Action Office for Drug Abuse.

Dr. Benson has also published extensively on topics in cardiology and related fields, such as the effects of meditation. In fact, he was among the first to do extensive research on meditation, and his reports on the subject have been an important factor in its current popularity. With Dr. R. Keith Wallace, he is co-author of a notable article entitled "The Physiology of Meditation" which appeared in *Scientific American* (February 1972). This article and an earlier one in *Science*, written by Dr. Wallace alone, awakened the scientific community to the physiological effects in the body produced by meditation, especially transcendental meditation (TM®).

For several years Dr. Benson engaged in research on the effects of TM®. His papers included reports on reduced blood pressure and decreased use of drugs. While performing this research, he also examined the literature on meditation research in general. There Dr. Benson found scientific and scholarly data about a variety of meditative practices in Zen, yoga, Sufism, Christianity, and Judaism. In all of these he found a technique that seemed to be one of the essentials, one of the common elements among them all for producing a quiet mind and peace of heart.

This technique involves repetition of a sound, word, or phrase. It is repeated over and over as the meditator performs his meditation. Sometimes it is said silently (as in TM®) and sometimes aloud. Also, the sound may have no meaning (as in TM®) or it may have powerful emotional and intellectual significance.

Dr. Benson feels that he has isolated this key factor and several others that various religious and spiritual traditions have discovered intuitively. Using his findings, he has devised a simple, nonreligious meditative technique for eliciting the relaxation response. In his first article, "Your Innate Asset for Combating Stress," from the *Harvard Business Review* (July–August 1974), he explains in simple terms how to use this method. At the end of the article he provides a brief survey of the traditions that he sees as using a similar method.

The Benson technique is easily learned. It requires only a few minutes a day, and can be performed almost anywhere at any time. The effects are both physiological and psychological. Anxiety and tension are reduced, along with their effects on the body that lead to ill health. Because of these obvious benefits, Dr. Benson has seriously suggested that companies do their employees a good turn by offering an alternative to the coffee break—the relaxation-response break.

The second article, "The Relaxation Response," is more technical. It originally appeared in *Psychiatry* (February 1974). Dr. Benson's coauthors were at that time a fourth-year medical student at Harvard Medical School (John F. Beary) and a premedical student at Amherst College (Mark P. Carol). The article is obviously intended for the professional community. However, we have included it here because it presents objective data from many sources in support of Dr. Benson's contention that the relaxation response is a sound medical rationale for the technique he has developed to promote physical and mental well-being. We have edited it slightly and deleted a complicated table showing the physiologic parameters supporting the existence of the relaxation response during the practice of various mental techniques. The essence of that table is presented as Table 1 in "Your Innate Asset for Combating Stress."

These two articles were originally intended for professional people: business managers and psychiatrists. But the information and the technique presented here are valuable for nearly everyone (including his Holiness Pius XII, whose remark at the beginning of this section shows a heroic attitude but a bad management practice). We are appreciative of Dr. Benson's permission to reprint the articles, and we suggest that you read his book, *The Relaxation Response,* for a deeper and more rounded presentation of his pioneering work.

YOUR INNATE ASSET FOR COMBATING STRESS

HERBERT BENSON

Emotional stress is a well-known aspect of the modern Western world and is especially prevalent in the business community. Our society has experienced rapid technological progress; the business community has been an integral part of this progress and, like the rest of the society, has experienced both beneficial and deleterious effects. Members of the business community have been forced to make certain behavioral adjustments—notably, a faster pace and a more pressured life—and behavioral adjustments of this sort induce stress. Although some individuals are aware of the physiologically harmful effects of stress, few know how to prevent or alleviate them. Victimized by the stressful world they have helped to create, many executives have accepted stress as a necessary component of their existence.

However, there is a simple way for the individual to alleviate stress and thus moderate or control many of its undesirable effects—effects which may range from simple anxiety to heart disease. The "relaxation response," an integrated physiologic response, appears to counteract the harmful physiologic effects of stress. It can be elicited by a simple mental technique.

The essential elements of the technique have long been familiar to man, and although they have usually been framed in the vocabularies of religions and cults where the elicitation of the relaxation response has played an important role, the response and the technique can be described in ordinary language. Moreover, the technique and the response can be beneficially applied by all the individuals of the community, including the executive.

The Concept of Stress

The concept of stress has been difficult to define and difficult to quantify.[1] Stress can be usefully defined through its physiologic correlates, particularly elevations in blood pressure Elevated blood pressure is consistently related to environmental situations that require behavioral adjustment by the individual and thus may be described as stressful. The behavioral adjustments associated with socioeconomic mobility, cultural change, urbanization, and migration are examples of such environmental situations.

Relevant findings were obtained in a comparison of high school and college graduates in managerial positions within the same corporation. The high school graduates experienced more general illness during the one-year period of observation and displayed more signs of cardiovascular disease and high blood pressure (hypertension). The investigators in this study postulated that the high school graduates perceived more threats and challenges in their life situations than the college graduates because of the greater discrepancy between their lives and their childhood experiences: the relative ill health of the high school graduates is regarded as part of the price they pay for "getting ahead in the world."

In other investigations, undertaken in several Pacific islands, higher blood pressure was found to be associated with the degree of Westernization. Migration from rural to urban areas in these same islands was also correlated with a rise in the prevalence of elevated blood pressure. Adrian M. Ostfeld and Richard B. Shekelle of the University of Illinois clearly summarized why these situations apparently require behavioral adjustment:

"There has been an appreciable increase in uncertainty of human relations as man has gone from the relatively primitive and more rural to the urban and industrial. Contemporary man in much of the world is faced every day with people and with situations about which there is uncertainty of outcome, wherein appropriate behavior is not prescribed and validated by tradition, where the possibility of bodily or psychological harm exists, where running or fighting is inappropriate, and where mental vigilance is called for."[2]

The Fight-or-Flight Response

Stressful situations that require behavioral adjustment appear to elevate blood pressure by means of a physiologic response popularly referred to as the "fight-or-flight response," first described by Dr. Walter B. Cannon of the Harvard Medical School. When an animal perceives a threatening situation, its reflexive response is an integrated physiologic response that prepares it for running or fighting. This response is characterized by coordinated increases in metabolism (oxygen consumption), blood pressure, heart rate, rate of breathing, amount of blood pumped by the heart, and amount of blood pumped to the skeletal muscles.

The existence of this integrated response in lower animals was substantiated by the Swiss Nobel laureate, Dr. Walter R. Hess. By stimulating the brain of the cat, he demonstrated that the controlling center for the fight-or-flight response is located within a specific area of the brain called the hypothalamus. When this area is electrically stimulated, the brain and other portions of the nervous system respond by controlled outpouring of epinephrine and norepinephrine (also called adrenalin and noradrenalin), which leads to the physiologic changes noted in the fight-or-flight response. These two compounds are the major chemical mediating substances of the sympathetic nervous system. Significantly, the overactivity of this functional division of the nervous system has been implicated in the development of many serious diseases. Thus the fight-or-flight response is an integrated physiologic mechanism leading to coordinated activation of the sympathetic nervous system.

A Czech scientist, Dr. Jan Brod, and his associates have demonstrated the physiologic characteristics of the fight-or-flight response in man in the laboratory setting. First, control measurements were made in a group of healthy young adults in a resting position. These subjects were then given a mental-arithmetic problem to solve: from a four-digit number like 1,194, subtract consecutive serial 17s. A metronome was set clicking in the background, and others around the subjects made statements such as: "I did better than that. You're not doing very well." Then new measurements were taken of blood pressure, blood pumped by the heart, and blood pumped to the skeletal muscles. All had increased.

Other situations requiring behavioral adjustment also lead to the fight-or-flight response. All humans use the same basic physiologic mechanisms to respond to individually meaningful, stressful events.

Although the fight-or-flight response is still a necessary and useful physiologic feature for survival, the stresses of today's society have led to its excessive elicitation; at the same time, its behavioral features, such as running or fighting, are usually socially inappropriate or unacceptable. These circumstances may lead to persistent hypertension. Those who experience greater environmental stress and, response have a greater chance of developing chronic hypertension (that is, chronic high blood pressure).

The Importance of Hypertension

High blood pressure, or hypertension, is of far greater significance to man than as just an index of stressful circumstances. It is one of the important factors—if not the most important—predisposing man to heart attack and stroke. These diseases of the heart and brain account for more than 50% of the deaths each year within the United States. Therefore, it is not surprising that various degrees of hypertension are present in 15% to 33% of the adult population of the United States, affecting between 23 million and 44 million individuals.

Heart attacks and strokes have always been diseases leading to death, predominantly in the elderly. However, it is highly disturbing that these diseases are now affecting a younger population. The late American cardiologist Dr. Samuel Levine pointed out that in families he followed for decades in which both fathers and sons experienced heart attacks, the average age at the time of the first attack was 13 years earlier for the sons than for their fathers. Many cardiologists feel that we are in the midst of an epidemic of these diseases. If hypertension could be prevented, this epidemic might be alleviated. Consequently, situations requiring behavioral adjustment, which may lead to hypertension, are of considerable concern.

The Relaxation Response

What can be done about everyday situations that lead to stress and its consequences? It is unlikely that the rapid pace of Western life will slow down significantly; and as far as our present standard of living depends on that pace, it is unlikely that most executives would want it to slow down. The need for behavioral adjustment will probably continue, and therefore individuals should learn to counteract the harmful effects of the physiologic response to stress. One possibility is the regular elicitation of the relaxation response.[3]

The relaxation response is an innate, integrated set of physiologic changes opposite to those of the fight-or-flight response It can be elicited by psychologic means. Hess first described this response in the cat. He electrically stimulated another specific area of the hypothalamus and elicited what he called "a protective mechanism against overstress [which promotes] restorative processes."[4]

Like the fight-or-flight response, the relaxation response is also present in man. Until recently, the relaxation response has been elicited primarily by meditational techniques the reader will find information about the effects of some of these techniques in Table 1. The practice of one well-investigated technique, transcendental meditation (TM®), results in physiologic changes that are consistent with generalized decreased sympathetic nervous system activity[*] and are thus opposite to the fight-or-flight response. There is a simultaneous decrease in the body's metabolism, in heart rate, and in rate of breathing. These changes are distinctly different from the physiologic changes noted during quiet sitting or sleep. Blood pressure remains unchanged during the practice of transcendental meditation; however, pressures appear lower in general among meditators than among individuals who do not practice meditation.

TABLE 1

Comparison of methods for inducing the relaxation response

| Technique | Physiologic measurement | | | | | |
	Oxygen consumption	Respiratory rate	Heart rate	Alpha waves	Blood pressure	Muscle tension
Transcendental meditation	Decreases	Decreases	Decreases	Increases	Decreases	Not measured
Zen and yoga	Decreases	Decreases	Decreases	Increases	No change	Not measured
Autogenic training	Not measured	Decreases	Decreases	Increases	Inconclusive results	Decreases
Progressive relaxation	Not measured	Not measured	Not measured	Not measured	Inconclusive results	Decreases
Hypnosis w. suggested deep relaxation	Decreases	Decreases	Decreases	Not measured	Inconclusive results	Not measured
Sentic cycles	Decreases	Decreases	Decreases	Not measured	Not measured	Not measured

A Very Simple Technique

The basic technique for the elicitation of the relaxation response is extremely simple. Its elements have been known and used for centuries in many cultures throughout the world. Historically, the relaxation response has usually been elicited in a religious context. The reader who is interested in the historical background of the response and its universality may enjoy the appendix to this article.

Four basic elements are common to all these practices: a quiet environment, a mental device, a passive attitude, and a comfortable position. A simple, mental, noncultic technique based on these four elements has recently been used in my laboratory. Subjects are given the following description of the four elements in the technique.

1. A quiet environment
One should choose a quiet, calm environment with as few distractions as possible. Sound, even background noise, may prevent the elicitation of the response. Choose a convenient, suitable place—for example, at an office desk in a quiet room.

2. A mental device
The meditator employs the constant stimulus of a single-syllable sound or word. The syllable is repeated silently or in a low, gentle tone. The purpose of the repetition is to free oneself from logical, externally oriented thought by focusing solely on the stimulus. Many different words and sounds have been used in traditional practices. Because of its simplicity and neutrality, the use of the syllable "one" is suggested.

3. A passive attitude
The purpose of the response is to help one rest and relax, and this requires a completely passive atttitude. One should not scrutinize his performance or try to force the response, because this may well prevent the response from occurring. When distracting thoughts enter the mind, they should simply be disregarded.

4. A comfortable position
The meditator should sit in a comfortable chair in as

restful a position as possible. The purpose is to reduce muscular effort to a minimum. The head may be supported; the arms should be balanced or supported as well. The shoes may be removed and the feet propped up several inches, if desired. Loosen all tight-fitting clothing.

Eliciting the Relaxation Response

Using these four basic elements, one can evoke the response by following the simple, mental, noncultic procedure that subjects have used in my laboratory:

O In a quiet environment, sit in a comfortable position.
O Close your eyes.
O Deeply relax your muscles, beginning at your feet and progressing up to your face—feet, calves, thighs, lower torso, chest, shoulders, neck, head. Allow them to remain deeply relaxed.
O Breathe through your nose. Become aware of your breathing. As you breathe out, say the word "one" silently to yourself. Thus: breathe in . . . breathe out, with "one." In . . . out, with "one" . . .
O Continue this practice for 20 minutes. You may open your eyes to check the time, but do not use an alarm. When you finish, sit quietly for several minutes, at first with your eyes closed and later with your eyes open.

Remember not to worry about whether you are successful in achieving a deep level of relaxation—maintain a passive attitude and permit relaxation to occur at its own pace. When distracting thoughts occur, ignore them and continue to repeat "one" as you breathe. The technique should be practiced once or twice daily, and not within two hours after any meal, since the digestive processes seem to interfere with the elicitation of the expected changes.

With practice, the response should come with little effort. Investigations have shown that only a small percentage of people do not experience the expected physiologic changes.[6] (However, it has been noted that people who are undergoing psychoanalysis for at least two sessions a week experience difficulty in eliciting the response.)

A person cannot be certain that the technique is eliciting these physiologic changes unless actual measurements are being made. However, the great majority of people report feelings of relaxation and freedom from anxiety during the elicitation of the relaxation response and during the rest of the day as well. These feelings of well-being are akin to those often noted after physical exercise, but without the attendant physical fatigue.

The practice of this technique evokes some of the same physiologic changes noted during the practice of other techniques such as those listed in Table 1. These physiologic changes are significant decreases in body metabolism —oxygen consumption and carbon dioxide elimination— and rate of breathing. Decreased oxygen consumption is the most sensitive index of the elicitation of the relaxation response.

Techniques that elicit the relaxation response should not be confused with biofeedback. Through biofeedback training, a subject can be made aware of an otherwise unconscious physiologic function, such as his heart rate, and learn to alter it voluntarily. He uses a device that measures the function—heart rate, for example—and "feeds back" to him information corresponding to each beat of his heart. He can then be rewarded (or reward himself) for increases or decreases in his heart rate and thus learn partial heart rate control Other physiologic functions that have been shown partially controllable through biofeedback are blood pressure. skin temperature, muscle tension, and certain patterns of brain waves, such as alpha waves.

But. whereas biofeedback requires physiologic monitoring equipment and can usually be focused on only one physiologic function at a time, elicitation of the relaxation response requires no equipment and affects several physiologic functions simultaneously.

Therapeutic Possibilities for Hypertension

I suggest that voluntary, regular elicitation of the relaxation response can counterbalance and alleviate the effects of the environmentally induced, but often inappropriate, fight-or-flight response.

For example, the regular elicitation of the relaxation response is useful in lowering the blood pressure of hypertensive subjects.[7] Individuals attending an introductory transcendental meditation lecture were asked whether they had high blood pressure and, if so, whether they would be willing to participate in a study of the effects of meditation on high blood pressure. Over 80 subjects with high blood pressure volunteered for the study. They agreed to postpone learning meditation for six weeks while their blood pressures were periodically measured and recorded to establish their premeditation blood pressures. At the end of the six-week period, the subjects were trained to elicit the relaxation response through transcendental meditation.

After at least two weeks of twice-daily meditation, the subjects' blood pressures were measured approximately every two weeks for at least nine weeks. Measurements were made at random times of the day but never during meditation. Throughout this entire period, the subjects were instructed to remain under the care of their physicians and to make only those changes in their medications that were prescribed by their physicians.

Of the original group, about 50 individuals altered the type or dosage of their antihypertensive medications during the course of the experiment. The data on these individuals were excluded from the study to avoid possible inaccurate interpretations caused by the altered regimens. There remained over 30 subjects who either did not alter their medications or took no antihypertensive medications. Comparisons were then made between these subjects' blood pressures before and after meditation.

During the premeditation (control) period, the subjects' systolic blood pressures averaged 140 to 150 millimeters of mercury. (Systolic pressure is the measure of the highest component of blood pressure.) After nine weeks of regular elicitation of the relaxation response, this average dropped into the range of 130 to 140 millimeters. Their diastolic pressures (the lowest component of blood pressure) averaged 90 to 95 millimeters during the control period and dropped into the range of 85 to 90 millimeters by the ninth week of meditation. These decreases reflect a statistically significant change in blood pressure, from what is considered the borderline hypertensive range to the normal range of blood pressure.[8]

An equally important result of the experiment was the change in blood pressure in the subjects who chose to stop meditation. Within four weeks both their systolic and their diastolic pressures had returned to their initial hypertensive levels.

Work remains to be done in this area, but these studies suggest that the regular elicitation of the relaxation response may be another means of lowering blood pressure. At the present time, standard medical therapy for hypertension involves the use of antihypertensive drugs. This pharmacologic method of lowering blood pressure is very effective, but it is sometimes accompanied by unpleasant side effects, and it is expensive. Indications are that the relaxation response affects the same mechanisms and lowers blood pressure by the same means as some antihypertensive drugs. Both act on the sympathetic nervous system.

Although it is unlikely that the regular elicitation of the relaxation response will be adequate therapy by itself for severe or moderate hypertension, it might act synergistically, along with antihypertensive drugs, to lower blood pressure, and may lead to the use of fewer drugs or decreased dosages. In borderline hypertension, the regular elicitation of the relaxation response may be of great value, since it has no pharmacologic side effects and might possibly supplant the use of drugs.

However, no matter how encouraging these initial results appear to be, no person should treat himself for high blood pressure by regularly eliciting the relaxation response. He should use the technique only under the supervision of his physician, who will routinely monitor his blood pressure to make sure it is adequately controlled.

Other Therapeutic Possibilities

Individuals choose various means to alleviate their subjective feelings of stress, and heavy alcohol intake, drug abuse, and cigarette smoking are serious problems in our society. In a recent investigation, 1,862 individuals completed a questionnaire in which they reported a marked decrease in hard-liquor intake, drug abuse, and cigarette smoking after they had begun the elicitation of the relaxation response through the practice of transcendental meditation.[9]

Details on decreased alcohol intake are as follows. Hard liquor was defined as any beverage of alcoholic content

other than wine or beer, and its usage was divided into
four categories:

1: Total nonusage of alcohol.
2: Light usage—up to three times per month.
3: Medium usage—one to six times per week.
4: Heavy usage—at least once per day.

Prior to the regular practice of meditation, 2.7% were
heavy users of hard liquor. This percentage decreased to
0.4% after 21 months of the twice-daily practice of meditation. Medium users comprised 15.8% prior to meditation; after 21 months they were only 2.6%. Light usage of
hard liquor decreased from 41.4% to 21.9%. Further,
heavy and medium users tended to become light users or
nonusers as they continued to meditate; and, whereas
40.1% were nonusers of alcohol prior to learning meditation, this percentage had increased to 75.1% after 21 or
more months of meditation.

The questionnaire also surveyed the drug-abuse patterns
of the group—that is, the usage of marijuana, amphetamines, barbiturates, narcotics, LSD, and other hallucinogens. Following the start of the regular practice of meditation, there was a marked decrease in the number of drug
abusers in all categories; and, as the practice was continued, there was a progressive decrease in drug abuse. After
21 months, most subjects were using no drugs at all.

For example, in the 6-month period before starting the
practice of meditation, about 80% of this sample used
marijuana, and of those about 28% were heavy users.
After regularly eliciting the relaxation response for approximately 6 months, 37% used marijuana, and of those
only 6% were heavy users. After 21 months of the practice, 12% continued to use marijuana, and of those almost
all were light users; only one individual was a heavy user.

There was an even greater decrease in the abuse of LSD.
Before starting the practice of meditation, 48% of the subjects had used LSD, and of these about 14% were heavy
users (at least once per week). After 3 months of meditation, 12% of the subjects still took LSD, but after 21
months only 3% still took it.

For other drugs there were similar increases in numbers
of nonusers after starting the practice of meditation. After
21 months, nonusers of the other hallucinogens rose
from 61% to 96%; for the narcotics, from 83% to 99%;

for the amphetamines, from 68% to 99%; and from the barbiturates, from 83% to 99%.

The smoking habits of the subjects also changed. Approximately 48% smoked cigarettes before starting meditation, and 27% of the sample were heavy users (at least one pack per day). After 21 months of meditation, only 16% still smoked cigarettes, and only 5.8% were heavy smokers.

This particular investigation was biased in several ways. The data were retrospective and subject to the limitation of personal recall. The group was not a random sample, nor was it chosen to be representative of the general population. Further, there was no control population; there are no data concerning the patterns of alcohol intake, drug abuse, and cigarette smoking of a matched sample of non-meditators. Only a prospective investigation can eliminate these biases. However, these data, as well as data from the other studies cited, suggest strongly that a beneficial effect may be derived from elicitation of the relaxation response.

I must emphasize again, however, that the relaxation response should not be viewed as a potential panacea for medical problems. An investigation of the response in the therapy of severe migraine and certain other kinds of headache, for example, has demonstrated the response to be of limited usefulness in these illnesses; it is recommended that this particular therapy be tried when other therapies of headache have proved unsuccessful.[10] *Thus, the relaxation response should not be practiced for preventive or therapeutic medical benefits unless done so with the approval of a physician.*

A Note on Side Effects

The side effects of the extensive practice of the relaxation response are worth brief discussion, although they have not been well documented.

When the response is elicited for two limited daily periods of 20 to 30 minutes, no adverse side effects have been observed. When the response is elicited more frequently—for example, for many hours daily over a period of several days—some individuals have experienced a withdrawal from life and have developed symptoms which range from insomnia to hallucinatory behavior. These side effects of the excessive elicitation of the relaxation response are difficult to evaluate on a retrospective basis, since many people with preexisting psychiatric problems might be drawn to any technique which evangelistically promises relief from tension and stress.

However, it is unlikely that the twice-daily elicitation of the response would do any more harm than would regular prayer.

Benefits for the Business Community

As noted above, well over 50% of our present U.S. population will die of heart disease and related conditions, and these diseases appear to be attacking Americans at younger and younger ages. The frequent elicitation of the fight-or-flight response has been strongly implicated in the development of these diseases. The regular use of the relaxation response in our daily lives may counteract the harmful effects of the fight-or-flight response and thereby mitigate these extremely prevalent and dire diseases.

However. modern Western society has turned away from many of the traditional techniques that elicit the relaxation response, such as prayer. Our society has thus lost an important means of alleviating stress and maintaining equilibrium in a changing world. We can probably greatly benefit by the reintroduction of the relaxation response into our society.

Because of its far-reaching influence in our society, the business sector could take the lead in this reintroduction. For example. programs could be established in which time is made available for employees to practice the relaxation response. Voluntary participants could choose whatever mode they wish: a familiar mode, like certain types of prayer or the simple, noncultic, mental technique previously described. A quiet environment is desirable, but a person can elicit the response at his or her desk or at any comfortable seat. A "relaxation-response break" might be substituted for the coffee break. This may improve employees ability to deal with stress and increase their sense of well-being. Not only may such an application prove beneficial to the individual—it may have further, broader benefits and ramifications for industry as a whole.

For centuries, people have used various techniques to

elicit the relaxation response, but it is only now that we are
recognizing its potential physiologic benefits. The relaxation response is innate. Members of industry need only take
the time to bring it forth. Finally, in our society, the
executive certainly has the power to effectively champion
the use of this simple but remarkably salutary response,
by making time available to bring it forth.

Appendix: A Historical Note

The elicitation of the relaxation response has been a part
of many secular and religious practices for centuries.

In the West, a fourteenth-century Christian treatise entitled *The Cloud of Unknowing* discusses how to attain an
alleged union with God. The anonymous author states that
this goal cannot be reached in the ordinary levels of human consciousness but requires the use of "lower" levels.
These levels are reached by eliminating all distractions and
physical activity, all worldly things, including all thoughts.
As a means of "beating down thought," the use of a single-
syllable word, such as "God" or "love," should be repeated:

"Choose whichever one you prefer, or if you like, choose
another that suits your taste, provided that it is of one
syllable. And clasp this word tightly in your heart so that
it never leaves it no matter what may happen. This word
shall be your shield and your spear. . . . With this word
you shall strike down thoughts of every kind and drive
them beneath the cloud of forgetting. After that, if any
thoughts should press upon you . . . answer him with this
word only and with no other words."

According to the writer, there will be moments when
"every created thing may suddenly and completely be forgotten. But immediately after each stirring, because of the
corruption of the flesh, [the soul] drops down again to some
thought or some deed." An important instruction for success is "do not by another means work in it with your mind
or with your imagination."

Another Christian work, *The Third Spiritual Alphabet,*
written in the tenth century by Fray Francisco de Osuna,
describes an altered state of consciousness. He wrote that
"contemplation requires us to blind ourselves to all that is
not God," and that one should be deaf and dumb to all else
and must "quit all obstacles, keeping your eyes bent on

the ground." The method can be either a short, self-composed prayer, repeated over and over, or simply saying *no* to thoughts when they occur. This exercise was to be performed for one hour in the morning and evening and taught by a qualified teacher.

Fray Francisco wrote that such an exercise would help in all endeavors, making individuals more efficient in their tasks and the tasks more enjoyable; that all men, especially the busy, secular as well as religious, should be taught this meditation because it is a refuge to which one can retreat when faced with stressful situations.

Christian meditation and mysticism were well developed within the Byzantine church and known as Hesychasm. Hesychasm involved a method of repetitive prayer which was described in the fourteenth century at Mount Athos in Greece by Gregory of Sinai and was called "The Prayer of the Heart" or "The Prayer of Jesus." It dates back to the beginnings of Christianity. The prayer itself was called secret meditation and was transmitted from older to younger monks through an initiation rite. Emphasis was placed on having a skilled instructor. The method of prayer recommended by these monks was as follows:

"Sit down alone and in silence. Lower your head, shut your eyes, breathe out gently, and imagine yourself looking into your own head. Carry your mind, i.e., your thoughts, from your head to your heart. As you breathe out, say 'Lord Jesus Christ, have mercy on me.' Say it moving your lips gently, or simply say it in your mind. Try to put all other thoughts aside. Be calm, be patient, and repeat the process very frequently."

In Judaism, similar practices date back to the time of the second temple in the second century B.C. and are found in one of the earliest forms of Jewish mysticism, Merkabalism. In this practice of meditation, the subject sat with his head between his knees and whispered hymns, songs, and repeated a name of a magic seal.

In the thirteenth century A.D., the works of Rabbi Abulafia were published, and his ideas became a major part of Jewish Kabbalistic tradition. Rabbi Abulafia felt that the normal life of the soul is kept within limits by our sensory perceptions and emotions, and since these perceptions and emotions are concerned with the finite, the soul's life is finite. Man, therefore, needs a higher form of perception which, instead of blocking the soul's deeper regions, opens them up. An "absolute" object on which to meditate is required. Rabbi Abulafia found this object in the Hebrew alphabet. He developed a mystical system of contemplating the letters of God's name. Rabbi Ben Zion Bokser describes Rabbi Abulafia's prayer:

"Immersed in prayer and meditation, uttering the divine name with special modulations of the voice and with special gestures, he induced in himself a state of ecstasy in which he believed the soul had shed its material bonds and, unimpeded, returned to its divine source."[11]

The purpose of this prayer and methodical meditation is to experience a new state of consciousness in which all relation to the senses is severed. Gershom Gerhard Scholem compares this state to music and yoga. He feels that Abulafia's teachings "represent but a Judaized version of that ancient spiritual technique which has found its classical expression in the practices of the Indian mystics who follow the system known as *Yoga.*" Scholem continues:

"To cite only one instance out of many, an important part in Abulafia's system is played by the technique of breathing; now this technique has found its highest development in the Indian *Yoga,* where it is commonly regarded as the most important instrument of mental discipline. Again, Abulafia lays down certain rules of body posture, certain corresponding combinations of consonants and vowels, and certain forms of recitation, and in particular some passages of his book *The Light of the Intellect* give the impression of a Judaized treatise on *Yoga.* The similarity even extends to some aspects of the doctrine of ecstatic vision, as preceded and brought about by these practices."[12]

The basic elements that elicit the relaxation response in certain practices of Christianity and Judaism are also found in Islamic mysticism or Sufism. Sufism developed in reaction to the external rationalization of Islam and made use of intuitive and emotional faculties which are claimed to be dormant until utilized through training under the guidance of a teacher. The method of employing these faculties is known as Dhikr. It is a means of excluding distractions and of drawing nearer to God by the constant repetition of His name, either silently or aloud, and by rhythmic breathing. Music, musical poems, and dance are also employed in their ritual of Dhikr, for it was noticed that they could help induce states of ecstasy.

Originally, Dhikr was only practiced by the members of the society who made a deliberate choice to redirect their lives to God as the preliminary step in the surrender of the will. Upon initiation into his order, the initiate received the *wird,* a secret, holy sound. The old Masters felt that the true encounter with God could not be attained by all, for most men are born deaf to mystical sensitivity. However, by the twelfth century, this attitude had changed It was realized that this ecstasy could be induced in the ordinary man in a relatively short time by rhythmic exercises, involving posture, control of breath, coordinated movements, and oral repetitions.

In the Western world, the relaxation response elicited by religious practices was not part of the routine practice of religions, but rather was associated with the mystical tradition. In the East, however, meditation that elicited the relaxation response was developed much earlier and became a major element in religion as well as in every-day life. Writings from Indian scriptures, the Upanishads, dated sixth century B.C., note that individuals might attain "a unified state with the Brahman [the Deity] by means of restraint of breath, withdrawal of senses, meditation, concentration contemplation, and absorption."

There is a multitude of Eastern religions and ways of life, including Zen and yoga with their many variants, which can elicit the relaxation response. They employ mental and physical methods, including the repetition of a word or sound, the exclusion of meaningful thoughts, a quiet environment, a comfortable position, and they stress the importance of a trained teacher. One of the meditative practices of Zen Buddhism, Zazen, employs a yogalike technique of the coupling of respiration and counting to ten, e.g., one on inhaling, two on exhaling, and so on, to ten. With time, one stops counting and simply "follows the breath" in order to achieve a state of no thought, no feeling, to be completely in nothing.

Shintoism and Taoism are important religions of Japan and China. A method of prayer in Shintoism consists of sitting quietly, inspiring through the nose, holding inspiration for a short time, and expiring through the mouth, with eyes directed toward a mirror at their level. Throughout the exercise, the priest repeats ten numbers, or sacred words, pronounced according to the traditional religious teachings. Fujisawa noted, "It is interesting that this grand ritual characteristic of Shintoism is doubtlessly the same process as *Yoga*." Taoism, one of the traditional religions of China, employs, in addition to methods similar to Shinto, concentration on nothingness to achieve absolute tranquility.

Similar meditational practices are found in practically every culture of man. Shamanism is a form of mysticism associated with feelings of ecstasy and is practiced in conjunction with tribal religions in North and South America, Indonesia, Oceania, Africa, Siberia, and Japan. Each shaman has a song or chant to bring on trances, usually entering into solitude to do so. Music, especially the drum, plays an important part in Shamanistic trances.

Many less traditional religious practices are flourishing in the United States. One aim of the practices is achievement of an altered state of consciousness, which is induced by techniques similar to those that elicit the relaxation response. Subud, Nichiren Sho Shu, Hare Krishna, Scientology, Black Muslimism, the Meher Baba group, and the Association for Research and Enlightenment are but a few of these.

In addition to techniques that elicit the relaxation response within a religious context, secular techniques also exist. The so-called nature mystics have been able to elicit the relaxation response by immersing themselves in quiet, often in the quiet of nature. Wordsworth believed that when his mind was freed from preoccupation with disturbing objects, petty cares, "little enmities and low desires," he could reach a condition of equilibrium, which he describes as a "wise passiveness" or "a happy stillness of the mind." Wordsworth believed that anyone could deliberately induce this condition in himself by a kind of relaxation of the will. Thoreau made many references to such feelings attained by sitting for hours alone with nature. Indeed, Thoreau compares himself to a yogi. William James describes similar experiences. For the reader who wishes to pursue the topic further, a treatise on other such experiences may be found in Raynor C. Johnson's *Watcher on the Hills* (Mystic, Connecticut: Lawrence Verry Inc., 1951).

NOTES

1. Mary C. Gutmann and Herbert Benson, "Interaction of Environmental Factors and Systemic Arterial Blood Pressure: A Review," *Medicine,* November 1971, p. 543.
2. "Psychological Variables and Blood Pressure," in *The Epidemiology of Hypertension,* edited by J. Stamler, R. Stamler, and T. N. Pullman (New York: Grune and Stratton, 1967), p. 321.
3. See Herbert Benson, John F. Beary, and Mark P. Carol, "The Relaxation Response," *Psychiatry,* February 1974, p. 37.
4. Walter R. Hess, *Functional Organization of the Diencephalon* (New York: Grune and Stratton, 1957), p. 40.
5. See R. Keith Wallace, Herbert Benson, and Archie F. Wilson, "A Wakeful Hypometabolic Physiologic State," *American Journal of Physiology,* September 1971, p. 795; see also R. Keith Wallace and Herbert Benson, "The Physiology of Meditation," *Scientific American,* February 1972, p. 84.
6. See Wallace, Benson, and Wilson, op. cit.; see also John F. Beary and Herbert Benson, "A Simple Psychophysiologic Technique Which Elicits the Hypometabolic Changes of the Relaxation Response," *Psychosomatic Medicine,* March–April 1974, p. 115.
7. See Herbert Benson, Barbara R. Marzetta, and Bernard A. Rosner, "Decreased Blood Pressure Associated With the Regular Elicitation of the Relaxation Response: A Study of Hypertensive Subjects," in *Contemporary Problems in Cardiology,* Vol. I: *Stress and the Heart,* edited by R. S. Eliot (Mt. Kisco, New York: Futura, 1974), p. 293; see also Herbert Benson, Bernard A. Rosner, Barbara R. Marzetta, and Helen Klemchuk, "Decreased Blood-Pressure in Pharmacologically Treated Hypertensive Patients Who Regularly Elicited the Relaxation Response," *The Lancet,* February 23, 1974, p. 289.
8. Ibid.
9. Herbert Benson and R. Keith Wallace, "Decreased Drug Abuse With Transcendental Meditation—A Study of 1,862 Subjects," in *Drug Abuse—Proceedings of the International Conference,* edited by C.J.D. Zarafonetis (Philadelphia: Lea and Febiger, 1972), p. 369.
10. Herbert Benson, Helen Klemchuk, and John R. Graham, "The Usefulness of the Relaxation Response in the Therapy of Headache," to be published in 1974 in *Headache.*

11. From *the World of the Cabbalah* (New York: Philosophical Library, 1954), p. 9.
12. *Major Trends in Jewish Mysticism* (New York: Schocken Books, 1967), p. 139.

THE RELAXATION RESPONSE

HERBERT BENSON, JOHN F. BEARY, AND MARK P. CAROL

In the Western world today, there is a growing interest in nonpharmacological, self-induced, altered states of consciousness because of their alleged benefits of better mental and physical health and improved ability to deal with tension and stress. During the experience of one of these states, individuals claim to have feelings of increased creativity, of infinity, and of immortality; they have an evangelistic sense of mission, and report that mental and physical suffering vanish (Dean). Subjective and objective data exist which support the hypothesis that an integrated central nervous system reaction, the *"relaxation response,"* underlies this altered state of consciousness. Physicians should be knowledgeable of the physiologic changes and possible health benefits of the relaxation response.

The Physiology of the Relaxation Response

The relaxation response appears to be an integrated hypothalamic response which results in generalized decreased sympathetic-nervous-system activity, and perhaps also increased parasympathetic activity. This response, termed the "trophotropic response," was first described by Hess in the cat (Hess, 1957). The trophotropic *zone* is located in the area of the anterior hypothalamus. It extends into the supra- and pre-optic areas, septum, and inferior lateral thalamus. The response is mediated by the parasympathetic nervous system and electrical stimulation of this zone results in hypo- or adynamia of skeletal musculature, decreased blood pressure, decreased respiratory rate, and pupil constriction. Hess stated, "Let us repeat at this point that we are actually dealing with a protective mechanism against overstress belonging to the trophotropic-endophylactic system and promoting restorative processes. We emphasize that these adynamic effects are opposed to ergotropic reactions which are oriented toward increased oxidative metabolism and utilization of energy" (1957, p. 40). The "ergotropic" reactions of Hess correspond to the "emergency reaction" first described by Cannon, popularly referred to as the fight-or-flight response and also called the "defense reaction" by others (Hess and Brugger; Abrahams et al.).

To better understand the relaxation response (the trophotropic response), a discussion of its counterpart, the fight-or-flight response (the ergotropic response), is appropriate. The ergotropic *zone* extends from the anterior midbrain toward the hypothalamus. The response is mediated by the sympathetic nervous system. When the zone is electrically stimulated, it consistently produces dilation of the pupils, increased blood pressure, increased respiratory rate, and heightened motor excitability. Although at times one of these responses may be emphasized, Hess stresses that there are no foci that correspond to individual isolated responses such as in the cortical motor zone. Rather, "In the diencephalon, we are dealing with a *collective* representation of a group of responses which includes responses of the autonomic system as they make their appearance in the form of synergically associated mechanisms" (1957, p. 35). Cannon reasoned that this integrated response prepared the animal for "fight or flight" when faced with a threatening environmental situation. Man also responds to threatening environmental conditions or to environmental situations which require behavioral adjustment by a coordinated physiologic response which mimics that of the increased sympathetic-nervous-system activity of the fight-or-flight response, (Gutmann and Benson).

The relaxation response in man consists of changes opposite to those of the fight-or-flight response. During the practice of one well-investigated technique called transcendental meditation, the major elements of the relaxation response occur: decreases in oxygen consumption, carbon dioxide elimination, heart rate, respiratory rate, minute ventilation, and arterial blood lactate. Systolic, diastolic and mean blood pressures remain unchanged compared to control levels. Rectal temperature also remains unchanged while skin resistance markedly increases and skeletal-muscle blood flow slightly increases. The electroencephalogram demonstrates an increase in the intensity of slow alpha waves and occasional theta-wave activity. Muscle tonus, not yet measured in transcendental meditation, decreases in other relaxation techniques (Jacobson; Luthe, 1969). These changes are consistent with generalized decreased sympathetic-nervous-system activity and are distinctly different from the physiologic changes noted during quiet sitting or sleep. The changes occur simultaneously and are consistent with those noted by Hess.

The Technique of Eliciting the Relaxation Response

Four basic elements are usually necessary to elicit the relaxation response in man:

1 *Mental Device.* There should be a constant stimulus —e.g., a sound, word or phrase repeated silently or audibly, or fixed gazing at an object. The purpose of these procedures is to shift from logical, externally-oriented thought.

2 *Passive Attitude.* If distracting thoughts do occur during the repetition or gazing, they should be disregarded and one's attention should be redirected to the technique. One should not worry about how well he is performing the technique.

3 *Decreased Muscle Tonu*s. The subject should be in a comfortable posture so that minimal muscular work is required.

4 *Quiet Environment.* A quiet environment with decreased environmental stimuli should be chosen. Most techniques instruct the practitioner to close his eyes. A place of worship is often suitable, as is a quiet room.

The efficiency of learning the various relaxation techniques appears enhanced when taught by trained instructors. . . .

Objective Data Supporting the Widespread Existence of the Relaxation Response

Physiologic changes occurring during the practice of

various techniques which elicit the relaxation response ... consist, in part, of decreased oxygen consumption, respiratory rate, heart rate, and muscle tension. Increases are noted in skin resistance and EEG alpha-wave activity. These changes are hypothesized to result from an integrated, hypothalamic response leading to decreased sympathetic-nervous-system activity. The neurophysiologic and neuroanatomic pathways from the cortex to the diencephalon remain to be defintively established (Gellhorn).

Autogenic training is a technique of medical therapy which is said to elicit the trophotropic response of Hess or the relaxation response. Autogenic therapy is defined as ". . . a self-induced modification of corticodiencephalic interrelationships" which enables the lower brain centers to activate "trophotropic activity" (Luthe, 1969). The method of autogenic training is based on six psychophysiologic exercises devised by a German neurologist, H. H. Shultz, which are practiced several times a day until the subject is able to voluntarily shift to a wakeful *low-arousal* (trophotropic) state. The "Standard Exercises" are practiced in a quiet environment, in a horizontal position, and with closed eyes (Luthe, 1969). Exercise 1 focuses on the feeling of heaviness in the limbs, and Exercise 2 on the cultivation of the sensation of warmth in the limbs. Exercise 3 deals with cardiac regulation, while Exercise 4 consists of passive concentration on breathing. In Exercise 5, the subject cultivates the sensation of warmth in his upper abdomen, and Exercise 6 is the cultivation of feelings of coolness in the forehead. Exercises 1 through 4 most effectively elicit the trophotropic response, while Exercises 5 and 6 are reported to have different effects (Luthe, 1969). The subject's attitude toward the exercise must not be intense and compulsive, but rather of a quiet, "let it happen," nature. This is referred to as *passive concentration* and is deemed absolutely essential (Luthe, 1972).

Progressive relaxation is a technique which seeks to achieve increased discriminative control over skeletal muscle until a subject is able to induce very low levels of tonus in the major muscle groups. Jacobson, who devised the technique, states that anxiety and muscular relaxation produce opposite physiologic states, and therefore cannot exist together. Progressive relaxation is practiced in a supine position in a quiet room; a passive attitude is essential because mental images induce slight, measurable tensions in muscles, especially those of the eyes and face. The subject is taught to recognize even slight contractions of his muscles so that he can avoid them and achieve the deepest degree of relaxation possible.

Hypnosis is an artificially induced state characterized by increased suggestibility (Gorton). A subject is judged to be in the hypnotic state if he manifests a high level of response to test suggestions such as muscle rigidity, amnesia, hallucination, anesthesia, and post-hypnotic suggestion, which are used in standard scales such as that of Weitzenhoffer and Hilgard. The hypnotic induction procedure usually includes suggestion (autosuggestion for self-hypnosis) of relaxation and drowsiness, closed eyes, and a recumbent or semisupine position (Barber, 1971). Following the induction procedure, an appropriate suggestion for the desired mental or physical behavior is given.

So far it has not been possible to find a unique physiologic index which defines the hypnotic state (Barber, 1971). Physiologic states vary the same way during hypnosis as they do during waking behavior. Suggested states of arousal or relaxation are accompanied by *either* increased or decreased metabolic rate, heart rate, blood pressure, skin conductance, and respiratory rate, corresponding to the changes seen when these states are induced by nonhypnotic means (Barber, 1971). If the control state is the same as the suggested state, then of course, no change in physiologic parameters will be seen (Barber, 1961). For example, the study by Whitehorn et al. reported that the control oxygen consumption value of 217 ml/min was not significantly changed by hypnosis. However, subjects in this experiment were trained to relax before control readings were taken. Therefore, hypnotic suggestion to relax produced no further change.

Sentic cycles is another psychophysiologic technique, devised by Manfred Clynes. A sentic "cycle" is composed of eight sentic states. A sentic "state" is a self-induced emotional experience, and the sequence of states used by Clynes is: no emotion, anger, hate, grief, love, sex, joy, reverence. A subject practices a cycle by thinking the state —e.g., anger—and responding with finger pressure on a key (which transduces the pressure for recording) as he sits and listens to a tape recording. The recording states which sentic state is present and when the subject should press the key.

Burrow described two kinds of attention: *cotention* and *ditention* (Burrow; Shiomi). Cotention is the subject's ". . . focus on the object of its environment." It is concentration on one thing exclusively. Ditention is described as "ordinary" wakefulness, in which state the subject's interest shifts from object to object. The state of cotention is induced by relaxing the muscles, closing the eyes, and resting them on a point imagined to be the center of a curtain of darkness in front of the subject.

Yoga has been an important part of Indian culture for thousands of years. It is claimed to be the culmination of the efforts of ancient Hindu thinkers to "give man the fullest possible control over his mind" (Hoenig). Yoga consists of meditation practices and physical techniques usually performed in a quiet environment, and it has many variant forms. Yoga began as raja yoga, which sought "union with the absolute" by meditation. Later, there was an emphasis on physical methods in attempts to achieve an altered state of consciousness. This form is termed hatha yoga. It has developed into a physical culture and is claimed to prevent and cure certain diseases. Essential to the practice of hatha yoga are appropriate posture and control of respiration (Ramamurthi). The most common posture is called lotus (seated on the ground with legs crossed). This posture helps the spine stay erect without strain and is claimed to enhance concentration. The respiratory training promotes control of duration of inspiration and expiration, and the pause between breaths, so that one eventually achieves voluntary control of respiration. Bagchi and Wenger, in studies of yoga practitioners, reported that yoga could produce a 70% increase in skin resistance, decreased heart rate, and EEG alphawave activity. These observations led them to suggest that yoga is "deep relaxation of a certain aspect of the autonomic nervous system without drowsiness or sleep."

Transcendental meditation is currently a widely practiced form of yoga. The technique, as taught by Maharishi Mahesh Yogi, comes from the Vedic tradition of India. Instruction is given individually, and the technique is allegedly easily learned at the first instruction session. It is said to require no physical or mental control. The individual is taught a systematic method of repeating a word or sound, the mantra, without attempting to concentrate specifically on it. It involves little change in life style, other than the meditation period of 15 to 20 minutes twice a day, when the practitioner sits in a comfortable position with closed eyes.

Zen is very like yoga, from which it developed, and is associated with the Buddhist religion (Onda). In Zen meditation, the subject is said to achieve a "controlled psychophysiologic decrease of the cerebral excitatory state" by a crossed-leg posture, closed eyes, regulation of respiration, and concentration on the koan (an alogical problem—e.g., What is the sound of one hand clapping?), or by prayer and chanting. Respiration is adjusted by taking several slow deep breaths, then inspiring briefly and forcelessly, and expiring long and forcefully, with subsequent natural breathing. Any sensory perceptions or mental images are allowed to appear and leave passively. A quiet, comfortable environment is essential. Experienced Zen meditators elicit the relaxation response more efficiently than novices (Sugi and Akutsu).

Possible Therapeutic Benefits and Side Effects of the Relaxation Response

Although advocates of many of the techniques which elicit the relaxation response offer anecdotal evidence to support claims of healthful and therapeutic benefits, only preliminary objective data exist at the present time which establish the place of the relaxation response in medicine. The regular practice of transcendental meditation leads to decreased systolic blood pressure in hypertensive subjects (Benson, Rosner, and Marzetta) and, in an uncontrolled retrospective study, was associated with decreased drug abuse (Benson and Wallace). The daily elicitation of the relaxation response predictably may be of value in situations where excessive sympathetic activity is present, situations which chronically evoke the fight-or-flight response and which may lead to prevalent, serious diseases such as hypertension (Gutmann and Benson).

The side effects of the chronic practice of the relaxation response have not been well documented. When the response is elicited for two limited daily periods of 20 to 30 minutes, no adverse side effects have been observed (personal observations, H.B.). When elicited more frequently, some subjects experience a withdrawal from life and symptoms which range in severity from insomnia to psychotic manifestations, often with hallucinatory behavior (personal observations, H.B.; Ornstein). These side effects are difficult to evaluate on a retrospective basis since many people with preexisting psychiatric problems would be drawn to any technique which evangelistically promises relief from tension and stress. Extensive prospective investigations of the relaxation response are underway in subjects suffering from hypertension, headache, drug abuse, psychoses, and anxiety neuroses, and results soon should be available.

If the relaxation response proves to be of value in medicine, there exist many religious, secular, or "therapeutic" techniques which elicit it. This should not be construed so as to interpret religion in mechanistic terms. *Belief* in the technique in question may well be a very important factor in the elicitation of the relaxation response. Future studies should establish the most efficient method for a given individual.

REFERENCES

Abrahams, V. C., et al. "Active Muscle Vasodilatation Produced by Stimulation of the Brain Stem: Its Significance in the Defense Reaction," *J. Physiology* (1960) 154:491.

Allison, John. "Respiration Changes during Transcendental Meditation," *Lancet* (1970) 1:833–834.

Anand, B. K., et al. "Studies on Shri Ramananda Yogi during His Stay in an Air-tight Box," *Indian J. Med. Res.* (1961) 49:82–89.

Bagchi, B. K., and M. A. Wenger. "Electrophysiological Correlations of Some Yoga Exercises." *Electroencephalog. Clin. Neurophysiology* (1957) Suppl. 7:132–149.

Barber, Theodore X. "Physiological Effects of Hypnosis," *Psychol. Bull.* (1961) 58:390–419.

———. "Physiological Effects of Hypnosis and Suggestion," in *Biofeedback and Self-Control 1970*. Aldine-Atherton, 1971.

Benson, Herbert, and Robert K. Wallace. "Decreased Drug Abuse with Transcendental Meditation—A Study of 1,862 Subjects," in C.J.D. Zarafonetis (Ed.), *Drug Abuse—Pro-*

ceedings of the International Conference. Lea and Febiger, 1972.

Benson, Herbert, Bernard A. Rosner and Barbara R. Marzetta. "Decreased Systolic Blood Pressure in Hypertensive Subjects Who Practiced Meditation," *J. Clin. Invest.* (1973) 52:8a.

Bokser, Rabbi Ben Zion. *From the World of the Cabbalah.* Philosophical Library, 1954.

Burrow, Trigant. "Kymograph Studies of Physiological (Respiratory) Concomitants in Two Types of Attentional Adaptation," *Nature* (1938) 142:156.

Cannon, Walter B. "The Emergency Function of the Adrenal Medulla in Pain and the Major Emotions," *Amer. J. Physiology* (1941) 33:356.

Clynes, Manfred. "Toward a View of Man," in M. Clynes and J. Milsum (Eds.), *Biomedical Engineering Systems;* McGraw-Hill, 1970.

Crasilneck, Harold B., and James A. Hall. "Physiological Changes Associated with Hypnosis: A Review of the Literature Since 1948," *Internat. J. Clin. and Exp. Hypnosis* (1959) 7:9–50.

Davis, R. C., and J. R. Kantor. "Skin Resistance During Hypnotic States," *J. General Psychology* (1935) 13:62–81.

Dean, Stanley R. "Is There an Ultraconscious Beyond the Unconscious?," *Canadian Psychiatric Assn. J.* (1970) 15:57–61.

Dudley, Donald L., et al. "Changes in Respiration Associated with Hypnotically Induced Emotion, Pain, and Exercise," *Psychosomatic Medicine* (1963) 26:46–57.

Estabrooks, G. H. "The Psychogalvanic Reflex in Hypnosis," *J. General Psychology* (1930) 3:150–157.

Fujisawa, Chikao. *Zen and Shinto.* Philosophical Library, 1959.

Gellhorn, Ernst. *Principles of Autonomic-Somatic Interactions.* University of Minnesota Press, 1967.

Gorton, Bernard E. "Physiology of Hypnosis," *Psychiatric Quart.* (1949) 23:317–343 and 457–485.

Gutmann, Mary C., and Herbert Benson. "Interaction of Environmental Factors and Systemic Arterial Blood Pressure: A Review," *Medicine* (1971) 50:543–553.

Hess, Walter R. *Functional Organization of the Diencephalon.* Grune & Stratton, 1957.

————, and M. Brugger. "Das subkortikale Zentrum der affektiven Abwehrreaktion," *Helv. Physiol. Acta* (1943) 1:33–52. Abwehrreaktion," *Helv. Physiol. Acta* (1943) 1:33–52.

Hoenig, J. "Medical Research on Yoga," *Confin. Psychiatr.* (1968) 11:69–89.

Jacobson, Edmund. *Progressive Relaxation.* University of Chicago Press, 1938.

Karambelkar, P. V., et al. "Studies on Human Subjects Staying in an Air-tight Pit," *Indian J. Med. Res.* (1968) 56:1282–1288.

Levander, Victoria L., et al. "Increased Forearm Blood Flow during a Wakeful Hypometabolic State," *Fed. Proc.* (1972) 31:405.

Luthe, Wolfgang (Ed.). *Autogenic Therapy,* Vols. 1–5. Grune & Stratton, 1969.

————. "Autogenic Therapy: Excerpts on Applications to Cardiovascular Disorders and Hypercholesterolemia," in *Biofeedback and Self-Control 1971.* Aldine-Atherton, 1972.

Maharishi Mahesh Yogi. *The Science of Being and Art of Living.* London: International SRM Publications, 1966.

Onda, A. "Autogenic Training and Zen," in W. Luthe (Ed.), *Autogenic Training* (Internat. Ed.). Grune & Stratton, 1965.

Ornstein, Robert E. *The Psychology of Consciousness.* San Francisco: W. H. Freeman, 1972.

Ramamurthi, B. "Yoga: An Explanation and Probable Neurophysiology," *J. Indian Med. Assn.* (1967) 48:167–170.

Ross, Floyd Hiatt. *Shinto, The Way of Japan.* Beacon Press, 1965.

Shiomi, K. "Respiratory and EEG Changes by Cotention of Trigant Burrow," *Psychologia* (1969) 12:24–28.

Sugi, Yasusaburo, and Kunio Akutsu. "Studies on Respiration and Energy-Metabolism during Sitting in Zazen," *Research J. Physical Education* (1968) 12:190–206.

Thoreau, Henry David. *Walden.* Princeton University Press, 1971.

Wallace, Robert K. "Physiological Effects of Transcendental Meditation," *Science* (1970) 167:1751–1754.

————, and Herbert Benson. "The Physiology of Meditation," *Sci. Amer.* (1972) 226:85–90.

————————, and Archie F. Wilson. "A Wakeful Hypometabolic State," *Amer. J. Physiology* (1971) 221:795–799.

Weitzenhoffer, Andre M., and E. Hilgard. *Stanford Hypnotic Suggestibility Scale.* Palo Alto: Consulting Psychol. Press, 1959.

Whitehorn, J. C., et al. "The Metabolic Rate in Hypnotic Sleep," *New England J. Medicine* (1932) 206:777–781.

III

HOW TO RELAX IN DAILY LIFE

Only two rules really count. Never miss an opportunity to relieve yourself; never miss a chance to sit down and rest your feet.

—*Duke of Windsor*

It should be clear by now that methods for improving your capacity to relax have been developed in every major culture. Science, in examining some of them, has found that impressive physical changes can occur through training in a specific discipline.

However, most of us have neither the time nor the desire to undertake full-time training in one of the major systems, such as yoga or Zen. Also, most of us are not under such severe tension or pressure that we can justify working hard to learn how to relax.

Relaxation should be relaxing—not another form of work. Ideally, work itself should be relaxing. In fact all our activities should be done in a non-anxious frame of mind and without tension-causing behavior. That is the goal to shoot for. This section offers a variety of approaches, techniques, and exercises to help you obtain that goal and add more relaxed time to your day. Nearly all the authors presented here have adapted their work from more formal and complex systems of physical exercises and mental training. All have streamlined their approaches so that people with no prior experience can make almost immediate use of the techniques.

We have two reasons for making these selections. First, they work well for people who go to an office or to a factory, for people who go to school, for people who stay at home. Second, they are easily learned from reading the instructions given. They are "how to" pieces presenting a range of possibilities to fit your needs—a sort of cookbook of relaxation recipes. (We have cut away the full explanations of why these techniques work. If you want to follow up on the core techniques given here, we have included an Appendix listing articles and books dealing with recent research. Also, the Additional Resources at the end of the book has useful items for further exploration.)

Are you aware of being tense? Are you conscious of when tension increases or decreases? Can you tune in to your body to sense, say, a tightness across your shoulders, a shallowness in your breathing, a coldness in your finger-tips, a tightening in your jaw, a pressure on your temples? People have been amazed and embarrassed as they worked with the practices in this section to learn how much tension they had without being aware of it. Even worse, they used to think that such a level of tension was normal!

Tension (in the sense of being uptight) is not normal. Tension arises when you incorrectly and unrealistically resist a stressful situation, either real or imagined. This is not an effective way to deal with such situations. Tension uses your muscles and your mind to waste motion, energy, and thought.

This is not to say that your life should be without difficulties, without surprises or reversals. *But these do not cause tension in and of themselves.* They are situations that you can accept, control and overcome if you act honestly and wisely. They are situations that can be either "problems" or challenging opportunities to learn and grow —depending on your mental attitude and manner of dealing with them.

Suppose you are angry with your spouse and have left home with the quarrel unfinished. Can it possibly improve your situation to clench your teeth, constrict your breathing, squeeze the steering wheel of your car, and improperly digest your breakfast?

Bizarre as it sounds, many people will actually claim that all this helps relieve their tension. But they're deluding themselves. Research has shown that these and similar tactics don't relieve the tension—they only *displace* it. They move the tension away from where it is obvious and easily dealt with into other less noticeable places in the mind and body. Doing this continually can build up habits over the years that actually maintain and increase overall tension.

When are good times to relax? Begin at home, using activities already familiar to you, so that disruption of your daily routine is minimal and the effects of your relaxation training are obvious. When you get up, when you sit down, while you are walking or running, when you stop working, during your leisure hours, and certainly when you are going to sleep—these are times to relax. In fact, every breath you take is an opportunity to relax and move from possible tension to relaxation, if you breathe properly. Several selections will give you the means to see for yourself whether you do and will help you correct your breathing habits if necessary.

What else can you do to relax? Mentally examine the situation in which you first find yourself becoming tense. See if your self-image—your ego—is in any way the source of tension. Were you uptight over "losing face" or angry over not getting your way? Were you attempting to dominate? Were you afraid of being pushed around? Examine the situation carefully and honestly to remove any personal input to the *cause* of your distress. That is a major part of the process of relaxing. It will bring long-term results.

Next, deal with the *effect*. You may not be able to fully resolve the situation immediately, but you certainly can stop getting tense over it.

The way to prevent yourself from harboring tension is to change your habits—to move from stress toward relaxation rather than from stress to tension. How? A great turnabout in your life isn't necessary all at once. Start with small things that can be easily integrated into your life. You'll find many such choices here—choices that are available to you from moment to moment.

Perhaps the stressing situations are more severe or longterm. Perhaps you fear losing your job. Perhaps you fear an illness common to your family history. Perhaps you're concerned over the way your child is relating to school or friends. Perhaps you have to deal with a difficult relative. In these cases, a more systematic, controlled approach to relaxation is desirable, such as meditation or yoga. Meditation is especially useful for detensioning and for a clear, calm examination of whatever part your ego may have played in the situation. It also can help you to find positive, creative solutions in problematic areas.

Relaxation is not an intrusion into your life. It can be fitted into those small moments when you are with yourself. The fundamental aim of this book is to help you make your life function better. As stress is being found to be behind more and more disease, so relaxation is the key to improved physical and mental health. This book can help you live longer and in better health by allowing your body to rest while in motion, to restore itself and to maintain itself for your benefit. The poetic advice of John Sullivan Dwight is most apropos here:

> Rest is not quitting
> The busy career.
> Rest is the fitting
> Of self to its sphere.

Enjoy what follows. It can add years to your life and life to your years.

DIFFERENTIAL RELAXATION

DAVID STUART SOBEL

Differential relaxation is a way to relax while being active. It involves learning to differentiate between those tensions necessary to perform an action (primary tensions) and those which are unnecessary (secondary tensions). By becoming aware of undue muscle tension in every-day activities and reducing these muscular contractions, you can achieve the greatest ease and economy in the expenditure of nervous and muscular energy. For instance, while sitting and reading this book, you can fully relax your legs, while maintaining only minimum tension in the specific muscles which are needed in order to sit and read. As you do any daily activity, ask yourself whether the various tensions in your body are necessary, and then reduce the unnecessary ones. After a period of time, this process will become automatic.

Now close your eyes for a moment and scan your body. Are there any areas which are particularly tense or tight or uncomfortable? We all have certain places in our bodies where we tend to hold or focus tension. Some people have tension centers in their necks, others in their jaws, stomach, hands, lower back, hips, chest, eyes, or forehead. Check your body again to determine just where you hold tension and then allow these areas to relax, release, and soften. If these tension centers are relaxed, your whole body will feel more at ease.

Try to remember to take a few rest pauses during the day and check your tension centers. Several minutes of conscious relaxation can quickly refresh and compose you.

From *To Your Health.*

LETTING MOVEMENT HAPPEN

DAVID STUART SOBEL

(Most people don't know how to get out of a chair. It doesn't take effort, it isn't a chore, and it doesn't get harder as you get older. The following is not an exercise but a way to take some unnecessary tension out of your life. It's fun to show this to people and watch them smile as they become aware of how easy it is. *Editors.*)

In movement, it is important to distinguish between the attitudes of "trying" and "letting." When you "try" to move, you often contract and shorten muscles unnecessarily. But when you "let" movement happen, there is a natural relaxation and lengthening which accompanies the movement. We tend, when we prepare to move, to tense muscles unnecessarily. Watch yourself as you get up from a chair. Before you actually get up, you will probably notice a tensing in your body, particularly in the legs, shoulders, and neck. This tensing involves a good deal of needless strain and wasted energy; instead, see what happens if you imagine letting your body rise effortlessly from the chair. The difference between these two ways of getting up is subtle; you may find that you can appreciate the difference if, in *letting* yourself get up, you let your breath lift you out of the chair. Inhale deeply into your belly, lean forward slightly, and as the wave of inhalation rises up through your body, feel yourself lightly rising out of the chair. To sit

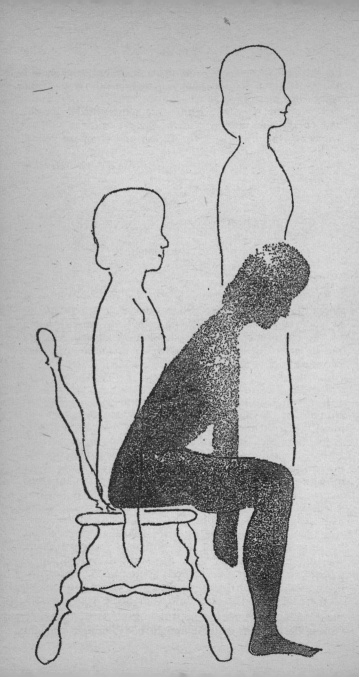

down, exhale and settle gently back down onto the chair.

You can let your breath help lighten and relax other every-day movements like bending, lifting, reaching, and so on.

From *To Your Health*.

RELAXED ATTENTION

ROBERT H. MC KIM

The Paradox of Ho-hum and Aha!

Relaxation involves loosening up, letting go, and finally —ho-hum—going to sleep. Attention involves focusing energy, finding excitement in discovery—aha!—and being very much awake. Ho-hum and aha!—what can these seemingly opposed modes of consciousness have in common? Together, how are they related to visual thinking?

Relaxation and attention are two sides of the same paradoxical coin. The first tenet of skill in any field is relaxation: the skilled always "make it seem easy." The second tenet is complete attention: expert practitioners invariably "give their all." Indeed, relaxation and attention are mutually supportive. By relaxing irrelevant tension, the individual releases full energy and attention to the task at hand. Watch any masterful performance—a rhythmic golf swing, a breathtaking ballet leap, a virtuoso violin solo—and you will see the importance of relaxed attention.

And so it is with thinking, man's highest skill. Relaxation is important to thinking generally, because we think with our whole being, our body as well as our brain. "Nothing," writes Harold Rugg,[1] "is more basic than the role of the body. We not only move with it, we think with it, feel with it, imagine with it." Overly tense muscles divert attention, restrict circulation of blood. waste energy, stress the nervous system: uptight body, uptight thoughts.

Be reminded, however, that the totally relaxed individual cannot think at all, even though awake. Physiologists have shown that some muscular tension is needed to generate and attend mental processes. Some tension, but not too much: relaxed attention.

The importance of relaxed attention to creative thinking is well known. After intensive conscious preparation, the creative thinker commonly lets the problem "incubate" subconsciously: "I will regularly work on a problem late into the evening and until I am tired. The moment my head touches the pillow I fall asleep with the problem unsolved."[1] After a period of relaxed incubation, which can take place in the shower or on a peaceful walk as well as sleep, attention is not uncommonly riveted by the "aha!" of sudden discovery. "Frequently I will awaken four or five hours later . . . with a new assembly of the material."[1] While subconscious incubation requires relaxation, a sudden flash of insight requires attention or is lost. Again, relaxed attention.

Memory, as Aldous Huxley[2] reminds us, operates in much the same fashion: "Everyone is familiar with the experience of forgetting a name, straining to capture it and ignominiously failing. Then, if one is wise, one will stop trying to remember and allow the mind to sink into a condition of alert passivity: the chances are that the name will come bobbing up into consciousness of its own accord. Memory works best, it would seem, when the mind is in a state of dynamic relaxation."

Ability to relax attentively is especially important to visual thinking. Excessive eye tension interferes with seeing; directed imagination is enhanced by a disciplined form of letting go; visual ideas flow most freely onto paper when the marker is held and moved with graceful ease. Even more than most human skills, seeing, imagining, and drawing require relaxed attention.

Optimal Tonus

Relaxed attention occurs when the relative balance of relaxation and tension brought to a task is appropriate. Bernard Gunther, in *Sense Relaxation*,[3] calls this relevant balance "optimal tonus." Edmund Jacobson, in *You Must Relax*,[4] calls it "differential relaxation." Both concepts describe the human organism adjusting dynamically and economically to the task at hand, never pushing or straining unnecessarily.

Jacobson describes differential relaxation in terms of "primary and secondary activities." He defines primary activities as those essential to the desired behavior. For reading a book such as this one, these activities include "contractions of those muscles needed for posture, . . . movements of the eyes to follow the words. . . ." Secondary activities are those that detract from primary activities: "While reading, a noise in the other room may be followed by looking up and turning in that direction." In dfferential relaxation, the individual differentiates between primary and secondary activities. He relaxes primary activities that are "unnecessarily intense for their purpose" and carries "relaxation of secondary activities to the extreme point, since these are generally useless."

Gunther emphasizes that optimal tonus, or differential relaxation, is "not letting go completely. Sleepy-sagginess-collapse is the opposite pole to hyper-tension." Excessive relaxation immerses the individual into lethargy or sleep.

Causes of Excessive Tension

An initial task in preparing to think visually is the reduction of excessive and inappropriate tension. When we tense our muscles, we do so to make a response. But why do we over-tense our muscles? What are the causes of excessive tension?

By far the most fundamental cause of hypertension is fear. The fearful or insecure person tenses his body because he believes that he will soon face a real or imagined attack or catastrophe. At work, he overreacts and burns energy needlessly, or does not act at all—in each instance, to avoid failure. At home in bed, he fusses and worries; his body tense, he cannot go to sleep.

Unable to relax, the fearful individual also finds it difficult to maintain attention. Every distraction is interpreted as a potential threat or an opportunity for relief. Easily diverted, he becomes prone to the conflicting mental agenda and immobile tension that characterize the indecisive.

Excessive tension has physical as well as psychological

causes. When energy level and muscular structure are inadequate to the response demanded of them, excessive tension results. The relatively unmuscular intellectual, for example, often lets his highly active mind place unsupportable demands on his ill-conditioned body, with resulting hypertension.

Josephine Rathbone, in *Relaxation*,[5] notes that "the person who is well and has nothing to worry about, who works consistently but without overeffort, who has sense enough to rest when he becomes tired, will never have to learn special techniques for relaxing. But how rare is that person!" Indeed, so prevalent is tension that large industries cater to letting go: alcohol, drugs, entertainment, health clubs, and vacation resorts. And when tension becomes untenable, we go to the "last resorts," psychologists and psychiatrists.

Breaking the Cycle

Jacobson, in *You Must Relax*,[4] persuasively maintains that physical-relaxation techniques provide an excellent way to break the cycle of fear, worry, and tension. Observing that physiological tests "indicate that when you imagine or recall about anything, you tense muscles somewhere, as if you were actually looking or speaking or doing something," he counsels that the individual should learn to observe the muscular sensations that accompany negative thoughts. Jacobson claims that by relaxing these muscular tensions, ability to maintain the negative psychological state is diminished. The totally relaxed individual, Jacobson has demonstrated, cannot entertain any kind of thinking at all, worriful or constructive.

Can the psychosomatic cycle of fear and tension be broken by deep physical relaxation? Possibly not without expert and sustained training in relaxation techniques, and, in extreme cases, probably not without additional expert psychological counsel. However, the experiential exercises that follow are nonchemical, free, available at any time, and relatively easy to learn. Try them. They are excellent preparation for visual thinking and may even have additional benefits.

Letting Go

Relaxation experts generally agree that the first step in eliminating excessive muscular tension is to become aware that you are tense. The next step is to realize that *you* are responsible for your excessive tension. The final step is to learn to let go of tension voluntarily. Ways of letting go take two forms: dynamic and passive. Dynamic letting go involves activity; passive letting go involves lying down and going limp. Most relaxation techniques combine both forms, as does the simple technique of stretching.

1. Stretch

1. Close your eyes and sit quietly for several minutes. Allow your attention to systematically explore the muscle sensations of your body: your face muscles, neck muscles, shoulders, and so on down. Where are you excessively tense right now?

2. Now, stand up and stretch—slowly, gracefully, and luxuriantly, like a cat. As you do, inhale deeply and feel the tension in your body.

3. With a generous sigh, exhale, sit down, and relax. As you do, feel the tension letting go. Sustain this passive sensation for several minutes.

Letting go of neck and shoulder tension is a special problem for individuals who "work with their heads." The human neck was evolved for the flexible side-to-side and up-and-down head movements required for hunting and survival. Holding the heavy human head over a desk for long periods while looking rigidly straight ahead at paperwork is a comparatively recent behavior that places an extremely unnatural demand on neck and shoulder muscles. These areas should be relaxed periodically, and always just before intensive visual/mental activity.

2. Relax Neck and Shoulders

1. Very slowly bend your head forward three times, backward three times, and to each side three times. Then slowly circle your head through the same movements, clockwise then reverse, three times each. Go slowly and

gently; most civilized necks are stiff. You will likely have to do this exercise several weeks before you can do it comfortably.

2. Pull your shoulders as far forward as you can, then as far up, as far back, as far down. Repeat three times.

3. With the fingers of both hands, massage the nape of your neck (near the back of the skull). Better yet, invite a friend to massage your neck and shoulder muscles gently with long strokes down along the back of the neck and shoulders. Then return the favor.

4. Take a deep breath and, with a sigh, let go excess neck and shoulder tension . . . more . . . more . . . passively let go.

3. Relax Arms and Hands

1. Sit or stand erect. Let your arms and hands hang loosely at your sides, like wet spaghetti.

2. As loosely as possible, shake your right hand. Extend this action to your forearm, then your entire arm. Let your arm rise over your head, shaking the entire limb loosely and vigorously.

3. Stop and compare the feeling of your right arm with that of your left.

4. Repeat with your left arm.

The importance of relaxed vision to visual thinking should go without saying. Tired, strained eyes interfere not only with visual thinking but with efficient mental functioning generally. Here are two basic ways to relax your eyes:

4. Palming

1. Precede this passive form of eye relaxation by gently massaging your temples and the nape of your neck and by blinking to lubricate your eyes.

2. "In palming, the eyes are closed and covered with the palms of the hands. To avoid exerting any pressure on the eyeballs (which should never be pressed, massaged, rubbed, or otherwise handled) the lower part of the palms should rest upon the cheekbones, the fingers upon the forehead. . . . When the eyes are closed and all light has been excluded by the hands, people with relaxed organs of vision

see their sense-field uniformly filled with blackness."[2] Put your elbows on a desk, or on your knees, so that you can hold your head comfortably on your palms for several minutes.

3. If you see any imagery at all in your mind's eye, your eye muscles are not fully relaxed. Turn your imagination to a pleasurable scene involving black: a furry black cat resting on a large black velvet pillow, or the night sky. You may have to palm your eyes several times a day, and for a period of time, before your inner field of vision takes on the deep and rich blackness that characterizes complete eye relaxation.

5. Facial and Eye Muscles

In this method of eye relaxation, you make existing tensions greater and then release them. By bringing muscles that cause excessive tension into awareness, you can then consciously let them go.

1. Wrinkle your forehead upward. Become aware of the muscles that are controlling the tension, and progressively let them go.
2. Frown tightly and let go.
3. Shut your eyes tightly and let go.
4. With eyes open, look to the far left, become aware of the muscles involved, and let go. Repeat looking right, up, and down.
5. Conscious of the tensions involved, look forward at a distant, then near object. Now let your vision unfocus and your eyes relax.
6. Close your eyes. In your mind's eye, imagine a bird flying from tree to tree, then perching quietly; a ball rolling along the ground, then coming to a stop; a rocket being launched, then disappearing into the blue sky; a slow, then very fast ping-pong match; a rabbit hopping . . .

Unfortunately, many methods for tension release are too conspicuous or time-consuming for people to use where they need to relax the most: at work. One exception is a relaxation technique advocated for centuries: deep breathing. We all must breathe, whether busy or not. The effectiveness of deep breathing as a method to release tension (and also to increase energy) is subject to rapid personal validation. Many deep-breathing techniques have been proposed. The following one is simple and reinforces the desired state by a kind of autosuggestion.

6. Deep Breathing

Slowly and easily take a deep breath, filling the bottom of your lungs as well as the top. As you breathe in, whisper the syllable "re." Pause for a moment, then breathe out, whispering the syllable "lax." Don't force the air in and out of your lungs; let it flow slowly and naturally: re-e-e-e (pause) la-a-a-a-ax (pause).

Deep muscle relaxation prepares the individual to sleep —"perchance to dream"—or, if mental alertness is retained, to imagine more vivid and spontaneous visual fantasies than can usually be obtained with normal muscle tonus.

7. Deep Muscle Relaxation

1. Lie down in a comfortable and quiet place.
2. Systematically (a) tense a specific muscle group (listed in step 3 below), (b) study the feeling of tension, and (c) relax, studying the feeling of letting go. If possible, step 3 should be read to the individual who is relaxing, the reader giving the relaxer ample time (and occasional reminders) to become aware of the feeling of tension and of letting go in each muscle group. The slash (/) signifies a pause.
3. Clench fists / Flex wrists (back of hand toward forearm) / Hands to shoulders, flex biceps / Shrug shoulders (touch ears) / Wrinkle forehead up / Frown / Close eyes tightly / Push tongue against roof of mouth / Press lips together / Push head back / Push head forward (chin buried in chest) / Arch back / Take deep breath, hold it, exhale / Suck stomach way in / Tense stomach muscles (as if someone were going to hit) / Tense buttocks / Lift legs, tensing thighs / Point toes toward face, tensing calves / Curl toes down, tensing arches / Review each activity above, letting go tension in each muscle group even more. Feel the peaceful, positive feeling that accompanies deep relaxation.

Devoting Attention

Letting go is often such an attractive experience that another reminder may be in order: no activity, mental or physical, can be performed in a state of total relaxation. Some tension is essential to attention. The goal of relaxed attention is to let go of chronic, excessive, or irrelevant tension, so that energy may be directed appropriately, freely, and fully. Devotion of attention is the focusing of energy. The vehicle for transmitting human energy is muscular tension.

There are many varieties of attention, however, some undesirable. In the military, attention is an order: "a-ten-*shyun!*" Too often the classroom also takes on a military air: several dozen individuals, despite large differences in personal interest, are forced to "pay attention," equally and together. When this external demand for attention becomes internalized, we force ourselves to pay attention. Externally or internally demanded, *forced attention* usually occurs for brief moments only, and must continually be reinforced.

Paying attention because you should or ought to is clearly less pleasant, and less effective, than devoting attention because you want to. The individual who attends because he wants to is not easily diverted. *Immersed attention* is natural absorption in developing an idea, contemplating an object, or enjoying an event. Watch a child pleasurably engrossed in stacking blocks to obtain a clear image of immersed attention.

Immersed attention should not be confused, however, with *passive attention*, which is being easily obsorbed. willy-nilly, in whatever comes. The passively attentive child who "seems to belong less to himself than to every object which happens to catch his notice" presents a formidable challenge to his teacher. Passive attention "never is overcome in some people, whose work, to the end of life, gets done in the interstices of their mind-wandering."[6]

Preattention is another natural form of attention. Absorbed in thought, for example, you suddenly realize that you have somehow negotiated your automobile through miles of turns and traffic without conscious awareness: you have been preattending the driving task. Preattention is comparable to an automatic pilot that attends routine events but cannot cope with the usual. Should a highway emergency occur while you are preattending, however, you must come to full attention to cope with it.

William James[6] describes another mode of consciousness, which he calls *dispersed attention*: "Most of us probably fall several times a day into a fit somewhat like this: The eyes fixed on vacancy, the sounds of the world mix into confused unity . . . the foreground of consciousness is filled, if by anything, by a sort of solemn sense of surrender to the passing of time." Unlike preattention, dispersed attention is not accompanied by another train of thought. Dispersed attention rests the human organism; it is a natural function of the attend-withdraw, tidal character of consciousness.

Of the kinds of attention discussed so far, immersed attention would seem at first best suited to visual thinking. What could be better than being able to "lose oneself," to become wholly immersed in what one is doing? Emphatically better is a quality of attention in which sense of self is not lost and consciousness is not taken over entirely by what one is attending. I will call this kind of attention *voluntary attention*. The individual who attends voluntarily is able to change the focus of his attention quickly, at will. To do this, his consciousness cannot be wholly immersed; he must be sufficiently self-aware to be able to decide.

Ability to direct attention voluntarily, and to sustain attention, is central to human freedom. "The essential achievement of [free will]," writes William James, "is to attend a difficult object and hold it fast before the mind." An idea "held steadily before the mind until it fills the mind" automatically steers behavior; when ideas "do not result in action, it will be seen in every such case, without exception, that it is because other ideas rob them of their impulsive power."

Like the art of relaxation, skill in voluntary attention can be learned. The first principle to learn is that you can fully attend only one thing, or related group of things, at a time. True, you can preattend one thing (of a routine nature) and attend another. But try to attend fully two unrelated conversations at a time, and you will find that you can do so only by alternating your attention between the two. You will also find that your attention naturally favors the conversation that most interests you, which

a sitting position on a bed, then lying back as soon as it has been carried out. Close your eyes and let your neck and shoulders be as loose as possible. Then rotate your head four times, very slowly, in a clockwise circle, trying to let the muscles loosen still more. Then reverse the movement, making it counterclockwise for four revolutions.

As soon as this is completed, you should lie back and immediately raise your right foot about twelve inches from the bed. Make the muscles as stiff and taut as possible, so they will tire quicker. As you hold the leg elevated, begin thinking of the muscles, following them from the toes right up to the hip. The eyes should be closed through the entire series of exercises. You visualize the muscles in your "mind's eye." By this means you have distracted your attention from the neck and shoulder muscles, so they will automatically relax completely.

Keep the leg elevated until it is thoroughly tired and it becomes an effort to hold it up. This may take from one minute to three or four. When it feels very tired do not lower it slowly—let it drop heavily, completely limp. This may take some practice to make it quite limp as it falls. The instant the right leg has fallen, raise the left one in the same manner, stiffening it. Immediately divert your thoughts to this leg, again following the muscles from the toes to the hip. Depending on the time it takes to tire the leg muscles, you may have to go back over the muscles in your thoughts two or three times, doing it very slowly. Then the leg is allowed to fall.

The right arm should immediately be raised into a Nazi salute position, but with clenched fist. Stiffen and tighten the muscles to tire them more quickly. Follow in your thoughts the muscles from the fingertips up to the shoulder and neck, repeating as often as necessary until the arm is quite tired. As arms are lighter than legs, it will take longer to tire them. As with the legs, the tired arm should be allowed to fall by your side as limp as the proverbial dishrag. The left arm is then exercised in the same way, the thoughts instantly diverted when the right one falls.

When the left arm has fallen, your thoughts can be diverted from it by imagining, with your eyes still closed, a circle on the ceiling above you. Imagine it to be about four feet in diameter. Follow this circle around clockwise with your eyes. Then reverse it and go counter-clockwise four times. This should be done slowly. Completing this, visualize a square instead, with sides about four feet long. Go around it in the same way, four times clockwise and four times counter-clockwise.

This completes the six exercises. You should then lie for a few moments enjoying the relaxation you have established. Divert your mind from the eyes by thinking of anything pleasant. Proficiency with this will come in three or four experiences with it and you will be surprised at the degree of relaxation achieved.

How to use this relaxation method. In order to learn the method, it should be done at least once a day for two weeks. It can be performed later whenever tension has developed. You are conditioning yourself to remain more relaxed during your daily life and will soon notice this effect. Of course situations which promote tension will arise but you will be much more relaxed between such times. Tension will no longer be chronic. You will retain nervous habits unless they are broken in some way, but they may be modified somewhat. Learning relaxation will also enable you to become a better subject for auto-hypnosis.

THE FEELING PAUSE

MIKE SAMUELS AND HAL Z. BENNETT

(This method of relaxation was especially developed to help you overcome disease, but it is a pleasure to do even when you are well. *Editors.*)

The feeling pause is a natural response which all of us use, without thinking about it, every day of our lives. It is a moment in which we briefly close off messages from the world around us, or *outside* us, so that we can get in touch with feelings that come from ourselves.

In many people's lives, day-to-day events demand so much attention that it's difficult for them to find the time and place to make decisions about problems of personal importance. They do not find the time to give as much attention as they would like to give to problems about their career, their style of life, or their family.

By developing your experience with the feeling pause, you can temporarily free yourself of the demands of busy day-to-day events; you can create an imaginary space in your mind where you can ask yourself far-reaching questions and get answers from your universal self to help you in making important personal decisions.

Developing the feeling pause for asking questions and getting answers is accomplished by imagining that the feeling pause is a real place, identifiable by sensation such as color, shape and touch. Actually, this is not such an unusual experience at all. Many people, when trying to solve a difficult problem, automatically let themselves remember places from their pasts where they went to be alone. One person may remember a room, another may remember a place in nature, where they felt secure and at peace. He or she might remember exactly how the place looked: colors, patterns, even smells, and tactile sensations. When they do so, they once more feel that they have all the time in the world, and the freedom to find answers to the questions which are important to them. They feel they are in a place where their questions will be answered.

Of course, not everyone has the good fortune to have a favorite place to remember and use in this way. But you can make a place like this for yourself. Creating this place in your mind will be similar to the experience of recalling the colors, shapes, and feelings of a place you once visited during a vacation trip. And the feeling-pause space will seem to become as substantial, pleasant and meaningful to you as the most pleasant event you can remember. This experience can then be used to help you develop other natural healing abilities.

In order to help you accomplish these things, we searched for an image which would be outside the realm of every-day experience yet clearly a part of it. We finally discovered this image in photos and narratives brought back to Earth by our astronauts and published in newspapers and magazines across the country. What better place than outer space to imagine oneself free of the concerns of everyday life!

You will find that in the next paragraphs we have included detailed instructions for relaxing yourself. These instructions are no more than elaborations of the yawn or sigh, together with imagining yourself resting, which you read about in previous chapters. These more elaborate instructions will allow you to take yourself a little further into a relaxed and restful state. Also, for reasons we don't fully understand, the experience of imagining oneself in space seems to create feelings of tranquility, expansiveness and openness for many people. And the physiological changes which can take place during this time are similar to those measured in people who are in extremely relaxed states, or who are meditating. Before reading the descriptive passages below, you may find it helpful to recall photos you have seen in magazines and on television which show you how the earth looks from outer space.

Choose a time of day and a place where you will not be disturbed. Lie down on a bed, or on the floor, or sit where you will be comfortable. Your legs and arms should not be crossed or cramped in any way.

Let your eyes be closed. Take a slow, deep breath, inhaling through your nose. Allow your chest and your abdomen to expand as you breathe. Feel the fullness of your lungs and abdomen as they fill with air. Now hold your breath for a moment. Then exhale slowly and enjoy the feelings of the air moving out through your nostrils. Feel your chest and your abdomen relax. Take another slow, deep breath, inhaling through your nose. Enjoy the luxury of this breath as though you were inhaling the delicious scent of spring blossoms. Feel your chest and abdomen become full. Then exhale slowly, feeling your chest and abdomen relax. Do this 3 or 4 times. Now let yourself breathe normally.

Feel your feet and legs. Imagine them becoming very heavy. Imagine your buttocks, back, shoulders, arms, hands, and head becoming very heavy. Imagine them being too heavy to lift. Enjoy this feeling of heaviness for a moment.

Now imagine what it would be like to move into outer space. Imagine yourself drifting weightlessly. Imagine the deep, pure blue color of space all around you. Imagine how the earth looks far in the distance.

Imagine stars and planets moving past you in the distance. Imagine yourself moving into a space of diffuse white light, as bright and ethereal as a distant star. As you approach this light, it increases in size until you feel yourself surrounded by its glow. Being in the light you feel that you are bathed in feelings of tranquility and clarity.

If disturbing thoughts or feelings enter your mind as you are in this feeling-pause space, allow them to pass by you just as you imagine planets and stars passing by you on this voyage. Let these thoughts and feelings fade into the distance, leaving them behind you in the same way that you might imagine a comet disappearing over the horizon.

Stay in this mental space for as long as you wish. Enjoy it as a tranquil resting space to which you can go any time you wish. When you want to return to your everyday state of mind, simply open your eyes.

The feelings of relaxing, then moving into space and being surrounded by a diffuse white light make up a subjective experience, an experience of feelings. Simply by reading the above paragraphs, you will probably find that you create a mental impression which makes the feeling pause similar to the memory you have of places where you have been. After you have experienced how it feels to imagine the feeling-pause space, you can recreate the experience simply by closing your eyes. You won't have to go through all the instructions again.

Some people have learned to return to the feeling-pause space by pausing, then listening for a high-pitched, high-frequency sound, similar to *ringing* in your ears. This is the natural sound that comes from *inside* rather than *outside,* but which most of us have learned to "tune out." Once you can hear this sound, by deliberately listening for it, hearing it will help you to move quickly into your feeling-pause space. Listening to the sound also has a relaxing effect on your body and mind and can help you feel tranquil when you find yourself in a busy or demanding situation.

THE ART OF CONVERTING ENERGY

LAURA ARCHERA HUXLEY

(Energy turned back on itself equals tension. Energy allowed to flow freely is relaxation. Understanding that energy is another way of describing feelings allows you to let it flow. *Editors.*)

Energy is neither good nor evil. It is a neutral power which can be used well or badly.

The art of living is simply the art of using energy in an intelligent and creative way. The purpose of this recipe is the conversion of energy—its conversion from a neutral power, or from a power that is being used badly, into a beneficent power, directed by intelligence and good will.

This recipe guides you in converting energy by a conscious act of the mind . . . The recipe is in five steps, the first of which is basic to the others. In this step, you are asked to make yourself aware of energy as a fundamental, all-pervading force, within you and around you.

You may do this by conscious direction of your imagination, or it may come over you spontaneously in a wave of effortless, intuitive realization. You may have experienced this fundamental energy spontaneously, at some high point in your life.

Wordsworth described it as:

A sense sublime
Of something far more deeply interfused,
Whose dwelling is the light of setting suns,
And the round ocean and the living air,
And the blue sky, and in the mind of man . . .

The purpose of the present recipe is to open the door to the experience he expressed in those beautiful lines. Here are the directions:

Choose a comfortable place where you can be alone and undisturbed. Read the directions several times until you feel that you have thoroughly assimilated them. They will be summarized at the end so that you can remember them when you put the book aside.

Become aware of the fundamental energy that is inside your body and all around it.

Think of the pure energy of the sun, of the oceans, of air, water, of the earth itself.

Imagine the enormous amount of pure energy concentrated in one small flower, in one piece of fruit, in a single seed which can become a forest.

What is your favorite form of natural beauty? The mountains? The sea? The graceful movements of a dolphin or of some other animal in its natural state? Think of this form. Let this image fill your mind. Think of the pure impersonal energy contained in it.

Feel the great life-force flowing within and all around you. Feel it in your muscles, in the coursing of your blood, in your entire organism. Let it fill you. Blend with it, until you and energy are one.

In this first step, the aim is not to understand but to feel energy. You may get this feeling immediately, or it may take a little practice. This one step alone is a wonderful energizer.

Now turn this experience of energy into a specific personal form.

Relieve a moment when you were filled with an awareness of energy, vitality, life-force, in a good and happy personal experience.

Recall a moment of great joy and harmony, of strength, or powerful creative energy. It may have been when you were walking freely in a forest or on a beach or when you were winning a contest; when you accomplished a difficult task acknowledged by many, or performed an humble but arduous chore unrecognized by any. It could be the moment when you first bite into a succulent piece of fresh fruit—or that moment when you are ready for, and know you are going to have, a fulfilling experience in love. It may be when you are doing absolutely nothing, and nothing extraordinary is happening, nothing except that you are aware of the ongoing miracle of energy flowing within you.

Relive your own experience, that moment when your whole being was swept and your vitality intensified by a wave of fluid, creative energy.

Relive it completely.

Now turn quickly to a moment when energy was destructive to you.

This may have been a moment when you experienced physical injury, when you saw someone else experience physical injury, a time when something precious to you was destroyed, a time when destructive energy was flung at you or others in words or actions, a time when destructive energy was silently communicated through ugly thoughts and emotions.

Choose one such incident out of your life.

Relive it.

Feel it. Do not just remember it.

Feel the impact of this destructive energy as you felt the inspiring flow of creative energy.

Let the feeling rise slowly in you. Or, if this comes more naturally to you, let yourself be engulfed by it, in an instant. Relive the incident from its very beginning to the final climactic moment of its destructive fulfillment.

When you have felt, completely and separately, these three forms of energy: impersonal energy, creative personal energy and destructive personal energy—you are ready for the fourth step.

Now you are going to alternate step two and step three.

Once more, let yourself feel that moment of personal creative energy.

Then, immediately, replace that feeling with the experience of destructive energy.

Let yourself go into the happy emotion; then switch into the bad one. Feel each of these experiences completely. Do not merely recall the events, but feel them totally, all the emotions, all the physical sensations.

For practice, it may help to visualize sharply contrasting colors: black and white, or red and green. Visualize white totally. Then quickly replace it in your mind's eye with black. Do the same exercise with sound, filling your ears with an imagined high, thin note, then replacing it with a deep, full bass note.

Now alternate your two opposite experiences of energy: the happy, creative moment—feel it completely; then the unhappy, destructive moment—feel that also, totally, in mind and body.

Practice until you swing back and forth between these two extremes in the experience of personal energy. The important thing is to learn to alternate quickly these opposite sensations, the total feeling of good with the total feeling of the bad, not the mere recollection of the events.

Repeat the preceding step. Swing back and forth once more between the two opposites of energy: creative and destructive, good and bad.

Now, quickly, by a conscious direction of your whole being, extract the good feelings from the creative experience and the bad feelings from the destructive experience—and float into the experience of pure impersonal energy as you did in the first step.

With full awareness, know that you are drawing out the good and the bad, the personal elements of each experience, and that you are letting yourself be engulfed by the impersonal flow of fundamental energy.

When you are able to do this well, you will find that you have gained remarkable power to direct your internal and external life.

Here is a summary of the directions to help you to remember them.

Experience pure energy.
Experience personal creative energy.
Experience personal destructive energy.
Experience in rapid alternation:
    Personal creative energy, then
    Personal destructive energy.
Repeat the last step, then rapidly return to the first.
Be sure always to end this recipe with the first step: fundamental energy.

By daily practice, you can become a CONSCIOUS AND INTELLIGENT DIRECTOR OF ENERGY.

In your daily life, in the midst of business, chores, activities—stop: and for just a few moments, experience pure impersonal energy.

Feel it.

And discover that *"Energy Is Eternal Delight."*

It works—if you work

From THE ART OF SEEING

ALDOUS HUXLEY

Relaxation, as we have seen, is of two kinds, passive and dynamic. The art of seeing includes techniques for producing either kind—passive relaxation of the visual organs during periods of rest, and dynamic relaxation, through normal and natural functioning in times of activity. Where the organs of vision are concerned, complete passive relaxation can be achieved, but is less beneficial than a mixed state, combining elements of both kinds of relaxation.

The most important of these techniques of (predominantly) passive relaxation is the process which Dr. Bates called "palming." In palming the eyes are closed and covered with the palms of the hands. To avoid exerting any pressure upon the eyeballs (which should never be pressed, rubbed, massaged or otherwise handled) the lower part of the palms should rest upon the cheek bones, the fingers upon the forehead. In this way light can be completely excluded from the eyes, even though the eyeballs remain untouched.

Palming can be done most satisfactorily when one is seated with the elbows resting upon a table, or upon a large, solidly stuffed cushion laid across the knees.

When the eyes are closed and all light has been excluded by the hands, people with relaxed organs of vision find their sense-field uniformly filled with blackness. This is not the case with those whose visual functioning is abnormal. Instead of blackness, these people may see moving grey clouds, darkness streaked with light, patches of color, all in an endless variety of permutations and combinations. With the achievement of passive relaxation of the eyes and the mind associated with them, these illusions of movement, light and color tend to disappear, and are replaced by uniform blackness.

In his book *Perfect Sight Without Glasses,* Dr. Bates advises the candidate for relaxation to "imagine black" while palming. The purpose of this is to come, through imagination, to an actual seeing of black. The technique he describes works satisfactorily in some cases; but in others (and they probably constitute a majority of all sufferers from defective vision) the attempt to imagine black frequently leads to conscious effort and strain. Thus the technique defeats its own object, which is relaxation. Toward the end of his life, Dr. Bates modified his procedure in this matter, and the most successful of his followers have done the same. The person who palms his eyes is no longer told to imagine blackness, but to occupy his mind by remembering pleasant scenes and incidents out of his own personal history. After a period more or less long, according to the intensity of the strain involved, the field of vision will be found to be uniformly black. Thus, the same goal is reached as is done by imagining black—but without risk of making efforts or creating tensions. Care should be taken, when remembering past episodes, to avoid anything in the nature of a "mental stare." By fixing the mind too rigidly upon a single memory image, one may easily produce a corresponding fixation and immobilization of the eyes. (There is nothing surprising or mysterious in this; indeed, in view of the unitary nature of the human organism, or mind-body, this is just the sort of phenomenon one would expect to happen.) To avoid mental staring, with its concomitant fixation of the eyes, one should always while palming remember objects that are in movement.

For example, one may wish to revisit in imagination the scenes of one's childhood. If this is done, one should imagine oneself walking about through the remembered landscape, noticing how its constituent parts change their aspects as one moves. At the same time, the scenes thus evoked may be peopled with human beings, dogs, traffic, all going about their business, while a brisk wind stirs the leaves of the trees and hurries the clouds across the sky. In such a world of phantasy, where nothing is fixed or rigid, there will be no danger of immobilizing the inward eye in a fixed stare; and where the inward eye moves without restraint, the outward, physical eye will enjoy a similar freedom. By using the memory and imagination in the way I have described it is possible to combine, in the single act of palming, the beneficial features of both passive and dynamic relaxation—rest and natural functioning.

This, I believe, is one of the principal reasons why palming is better for the organs of vision than any form of wholly passive relaxation. When the activities of the memory and imagination are completely inhibited, such wholly passive relaxation can be carried, after some practice, to the point where the eyelids and the eyeball itself lose their tone and go soft. This condition is so remote from the normal state of the eyes that its attainment does little or nothing to help in improving vision. Palming, on the contrary, keeps the mental powers of attention and perception at work in the effortless, freely shifting way which is natural to them, at the same time as it rests the eyes.

The other main reasons for the efficacy of palming are of a physical nature. There is refreshment in the temporary exclusion of light, and comfort in the warmth of the hands. Moreover, all parts of the body carry their own characteristic potentials; and it is possible that the placing of the hands over the eyes does something to the electrical condition of the fatigued organs—something that reinvigorates the tissues and indirectly soothes the mind.

Be this as it may, the results of palming are remarkable. Fatigue is rapidly relieved; and when the eyes are uncovered, vision is often noticeably improved, at any rate for a time.

When there is strain and when vision is defective, there can never be too much palming. Many who have experienced its benefits deliberately set aside regular periods for palming. Others prefer to take such opportunities as each day may casually offer, or as their own fatigue may make it urgently necessary for them to create. In even the busiest lives there are blank and unoccupied intervals, which may profitably be used to relax the eyes and mind, and so to gain improved vision for further work. In all cases, the important thing to remember is that prevention is better than cure, and that, by devoting a few minutes to relaxation, one may spare oneself many hours of fatigue and lowered visual efficiency. In the words of Mr. F. M. Alexander, we all tend to be greedy "end-gainers," paying no attention to our "means-whereby." And yet it must be obvious to anyone who will give the subject a moment's thought, that the nature of the means employed will always determine the nature of the end attained. In the case of the eyes and the mind controlling them, means that involve unrelieved strain result in lowered vision and general physical and mental fatigue. By allowing ourselves intervals of the right sort of relaxation, we can improve the means-whereby and so arrive more easily at our end, which is, approximately, good vision and, ultimately, the accomplishment of tasks for which good vision is necessary.

"Seek ye first the kingdom of God and His righteousness, and all the rest shall be added." This saying is as profoundly true on the plane of the psycho-physiological skills as it is upon the planes of spirituality, ethics and politics. By seeking first relaxed visual functioning of the kind that Nature intended us to have, we shall find that all the rest will be added to us, in the form of better sight and heightened powers of work. If, on the contrary, we persist in behaving as greedy and thoughtless end-gainers, aiming directly at better vision (through mechanical devices for neutralizing symptoms) and increased efficiency (through unremitting strain and effort), we shall end by seeing worse and getting less work done.

Where circumstances make it difficult or embarrassing to assume the attitude of palming, it is possible to obtain a certain measure of relaxation by palming mentally—that is, by closing the eyes, imagining that they are covered with the hands and remembering some pleasant scene or episode, as suggested in an earlier paragraph. This should be accompanied by a conscious "letting go" of the eyes— a "thinking of looseness" in relation to the strained and tired tissues. Purely mental palming is not so beneficial as palming which is both mental and physical; but it is a good second-best.

TOUCH AWAY TENSION

ANNE KENT RUSH

Everyone has some idea of the benefits of massage. Letting yourself relax while your body is worked over by a skilled masseur or masseuse can be a most pleasurable way of relieving tensions. But what about self-massage—can you relieve your tensions when you do the work yourself?

Yes, you can. And self-massage has some simple practical advantages: it costs virtually nothing, it allows you full control over pressure and speed, and you can have it almost anytime you want.

The benefits of self-massage. Our bodies are continually seeking that perfect relation between relaxation and stimulation, rest and activity, called balance. Various massage techniques for obtaining that balance have been developed in almost every culture. There are chakra massages from India, stone massages from Scandinavia, music massages from Burma, meditation massages from Tibet, and many others. The self-massage exercises I describe here, which draw on some of these techniques, are designed to help you reach your ideal balance in all your daily activities.

Self-massage is beneficial for health and beauty. It is an easy, natural way to improve your posture and your circulation. It also helps you to become more aware of your body and of the various tensions and stresses that may build up in it in the course of the day.

Through the body, self-massage helps the mind. The development today of a branch of psychology called "body therapy" is testimony to the increased knowledge we are gaining about the interrelation of our minds and bodies. (Through the technique known as biofeedback, for example, people who monitor their own vital functions can learn to change their heart rate or overcome insomnia.) Self-massage helps you to become more aware of your body and of the various tensions that may build up in it during the day. The self-massage exercises included here come from my studies of various body therapies and their exploration of the mental-physical relationship.

Good and bad massage. It is very difficult to harm yourself with self-massage, and most of the things to avoid are matters of common sense. If you are ill, ask your physician's opinion before doing any elaborate self-massage. Wounded or damaged tissue should not be pressed on too hard, but can be stroked lightly. Healthy muscles are safe areas to apply pressure on. Bones, nerves, and tendons are more sensitive than muscle tissue. The areas to which pressure should not be applied are: for women, breasts, and, for both women and men, the lymph glands. The most sensitive and accessible areas of lymph glands are under the jaw and at the base of the front and the sides of the neck, and also under the armpits.

Many people have the attitude that "it's no good unless it hurts." Applied to body therapy or self-massage, this is not a correct or an effective rule. If what you're doing in self-massage hurts you, lighten up or stop.

Pressure on a tense muscle can be very relaxing and beneficial, but only if applied correctly. Too much pressure applied too fast causes the muscle to tense up in reaction. But on the larger muscles you can apply very deep pressure, probably even as much as your strength and weight allow, if you apply it very gradually and in pace with the muscle's ability to relax with it. Use your body weight for the pressure, rather than tensing and pushing. Lean into the muscle with your whole body as though you were resting your weight on it.

If you are not sure whether a muscle is tense, see if you can move it comfortably and easily through its normal limits. Your muscles should be neither tense nor flabby—neither too hard nor too soft. For a guide to the correct consistency, feel the muscles of your forearm just below the elbow.

Breathing. One easy way to control your rhythm and circulation is by regulating your breathing. Slow, deep breaths, combined with rest or slow movement, have an instant calming effect on your system. Fast movement and faster, more shallow breathing automatically speed up your circulation. You can pace your motion and your breathing during your self-massage according to which body state you want to create.

The work of Magdalene Proskauer, a therapist in San Francisco, has influenced me most in my knowledge of the role of breathing in physical and mental balance. She teaches techniques for "letting your breathing massage you from inside" and encourages people to find their own imagery for this meditative internal massage. I find it particularly effective to imagine that my breath is ocean waves swirling through my body and relaxing my muscles, or that I can inhale and exhale through some body part other than my nose, such as "breathing through my hip joint." You can experiment with this form of self-massage on any body part, or even imagine that your body is porous and you are breathing through all of it.

What you'll need. An oil or cream is necessary to reduce friction and permit long, smooth strokes. You may want to experiment with different oils and creams by rubbing them all over your body, taking care to press harder on any tense muscles you discover. I do this simple self-massage after every shower or bath, when I would be applying body cream anyway. The basic requirements for a good self-massage ointment are that it should be beneficial to your skin and not sink in rapidly. For summer massages, one of the best ointments I've discovered is pure cocoa butter.

I spread a beach towel, or sometimes a Japanese straw mat, on my rug to lie or sit on. You can use the carpet or even do the exercises on your bed. A small cushion is useful to support the base of the spine. Because you will want to focus on your own rhythm, I would not recommend music since it imposes an outside rhythm.

Starting out. Choose a pleasant, secluded room in your home. Sit down on your mat or beach towel. Place the small cushion under the base of your spine to angle your body slightly forward. This eases the effort of sitting up. Sit comfortably, crosslegged, with one leg in front of the other.

As with any other activity, self-massage is most effective if you do some simple warm-ups, which provide a transition into the mood of your self-massage. Warm-ups can be as simple as sitting alone quietly with your eyes closed, to take note of your physical and emotional state. Take a few deep breaths to relax yourself and then give yourself a few moments to decide what kinds of tension you're under and what special needs you might have today. You may feel particularly tense in one place, such as your lower back or your neck, and want to focus most of your self-massage on this area. Or you may feel you just generally need to relax and want to do a complete body massage.

Part your lips slightly and breathe through your mouth throughout the self-massage so that the muscles of your jaw can relax. Let your stomach muscles relax and breathe so that you can see your belly move in and out. Scan your internal sensations for clues to where you're feeling tense and where relaxed. Preferably, keep your eyes closed throughout the massage so that you are guided by these internal messages. Don't be discouraged if the messages are faint or confused at first; they will come through more clearly with practice.

How much, how often? For maximum benefit, regularity of self-massage is more important than the length of each session. I find that two sessions a day are best for me. In the morning I usually do my self-massage in bed before I get up; around 5:30 in the evening I do it on the mat on the floor. Your needs for stimulation and relaxation will vary at different times of the day; this is where your control of rhythm and breathing becomes useful. In the morning I start slowly, with measured breathing, and gradually accelerate. In the evening, to relax, I reverse the rhythm.

Remember that regimented exercise is not the aim. Although I describe specific self-massage techniques that you will have to practice separately at first, you can soon find yourself performing them in a flowing sequence.

Scalp

Using the thumbs and fingertips of both hands, press as firmly as possible all over the back, sides, and top of your head, shifting the scalp. One way to create this pressure easily is to work your hands on opposite sides of your head, pushing your hands toward each other. Pay special attention to the center line of the top of the head, the temples, behind the ears, and the base of the scalp.

Face

Starting at the top of your forehead, use your fingertips to gently draw the skin over the bone in a downward direction; hold it down for a few seconds. Now release the skin, move your fingers to the next lower area of your face, and repeat. This gentle motion helps relieve the tension of facial muscles, which are usually straining in other directions during the day. It gives your face permission to go "slack" for awhile. Try combining your exhalation with the downward motion. Don't forget eyelids and lips.

Neck

Let your head relax forward. Place both hands on back of your neck where it joins the shoulders, and squeeze it firmly several times between your thumbs and fingers. Now, place one hand on your upper back, positioning your fingertips on the vertebrae of your spine between your shoulder blades. The other hand should rest opposite it on your chest. As you lift your head to an upright position, you should feel the movement of your spine with your fingertips. It is here—not higher up—that your head and neck movements begin. By thinking of this during the day whenever you move your head, you will help prevent much future neck tension.

The next exercise should be done with your eyes open. With your head upright and facing forward, place the first two fingers of your left hand over your head onto your right temple. While pressing *hard* on the temple, allow your head to lean down to the left toward your shoulder, and gradually let your whole torso lean down and forward, exhaling as you lean. Look at the floor. Balance yourself with the fingers of your right hand on the floor to your right. Inhale and come back to an upright position. Reverse and repeat on the other side.

Shoulders

Test your trapezius muscles (the large triangular muscles that extend between your neck and shoulders) for tension by exploring the area for hard lumps. You should be able to press as firmly on any part of your trapezius as you can on, say, your lower arm muscles without feeling hardness or achiness. Start with your left shoulder. When you find a tense spot, press gradually harder and harder on it with the fingers of your right hand, exhaling as you press down. After about 20 seconds, release the pressure. The hardness and achiness should be relieved, and you should feel a distinct relaxation in the muscle. Do this pressure-and-release technique all over your left shoulder muscle. Compare how this shoulder feels with the unmassaged side. Now work with your left hand on your right shoulder.

Arms

From Moshe Feldenkrais, an expert body therapist from Israel, I learned some excellent techniques for tension release and postural alignment. One technique stems from the fact that muscles get into habit ruts just as we do—and every now and then they need some unusual experience to shake up their routine. A simple yet effective way to do this is by twisting the muscles extremely lightly in a different direction from normal.

I particularly like this technique on arm muscles, since they are difficult areas to work on in other ways. Your arm muscles usually move up and down; disorient them by moving them sideways and around the bones. Let your right arm be as loose and relaxed as possible. Using your left hand, encircle as much of your upper inner arm as you can. Inhaling, gently twist that section of muscle around the bone, out and away from your body. Hold this position to a count of 15 while exhaling. Now open your palm and let the muscle roll back again.

Repeat this down your whole arm to the wrist. Then try your left arm.

Hands

With the thumb and forefinger of your right hand, squeeze the fleshy area between each bone on your left hand, about half an inch from the base of the fingers. Pay special attention to the area between the thumb and the index finger. Also pinch the area of muscle below the little finger on the outside of the palm.

Next, bend the index and second finger of your right

hand and use them to grip your left-hand index finger at its base. Pull firmly from base to tip. Try to make a snapping noise as your right-hand joints come off the end of the finger. Repeat for each finger, both hands.

Abdomen

The stomach area is an important place to massage to improve digestion. The intestines wind around a "square" area delineated by your ribs on top, your waist on both sides, and your pelvis on the bottom. As food is processed through that "square," it travels up your right side, across the middle, and down your left side. Follow this route on the outside as you massage your abdomen deeply with your fingertips, inhaling as you begin and exhaling as you apply pressure. Massage the square several times.

Back

One of the most effective ways to relax your spine is to use your vertebrae to massage each other. Sit cross-legged and lean to the left, twisting your spine as you turn. To help you twist further, use both arms to reach around on the floor and use your eyes to look as far in the direction you're turning as you can. You'll find that when you think you've gone as far as you can go, if you pause and focus your eyes on a more distant spot in the direction you want to move, you will be able, then, to turn a little further. But be careful to move gently, without straining. As you twist further, you can "walk" your hands on the floor in the direction you want to go. Eventually you can twist your spine at every vertebra by the way you change the angle of your body as you turn. Repeat, leaning in the opposite direction.

Now face forward again. Let your whole head, neck, and torso relax forward. Using both hands, position your thumbs on your front ribs and your fingers along your spine. Inhale and raise your hands as close to your shoulder blades as you comfortably can. Squeezing with your hands, exhale and draw them down your back to your waist, ending up at your hipbones. Release the pressure. Return to your starting point and repeat this downward stroking motion 5 times in rhythm with your breathing.

Hips and Thighs

Because we move our hips and thighs relatively little compared with other parts of our body, these areas often accumulate fat. Grasp an area of fatty tissue on your left hip and knead the area deeply with your fingertips. Now begin moving your hands in opposing direction so that you make an S-shape with the flesh. End this sequence with long strokes over the area in the direction of the heart. Do this sequence all over the tissues of your hips and thighs.

An easy and fun massage for your buttocks is to roll and "walk" around on them in a sitting position, using your body weight to massage the area.

Legs

In the sitting position, with your eyes closed, use the heels of your hands to lean your weight into and "walk" down the long frontal muscles of your thighs. Let your head and torso lean forward slightly as you massage so that your back and arms don't strain. "Walk" down each thigh several times.

Now use your fingertips to firmly massage the area around and behind your knees, moving the fingers in small circles. This is a critical stress area, which appreciates special attention.

For your calves, use your hands in a pinching manner on both sides of the shin, where your calf muscle attaches to the bone. Work down from the knee to the ankle, including the Achilles tendon just above the heel.

Feet

The feet contain nerve endings from all other parts of your body. Massage on the feet is therefore particularly soothing because you are, in effect, massaging your whole body, long-distance, through the nerve connections. (Experiment with pressure points on your feet and see if you feel a response in some other body part.) Using your thumbs, or even knuckles, press in different spots all over the top and soles of your feet. End by pinching the tip of each toe.

Whole Body

You have taken care of specific areas of your body. Now do some long stroking up and down your whole body to connect all your separately massaged parts. One pleasant way to do this is to begin with your palms on the soles of your feet and make long sweeping strokes up your legs, up both sides of your abdomen and torso, reaching your shoulders. Now let your arms continue the motion by opening out into the air, spreading your hands as you do. Inhale as your arms move up your body, and exhale as you let them float down to your feet again. Make these large, sweeping circles several times.

And, Finally, Resting

Resting is an essential part of your self-massage, since your body needs time to assimilate the results of your experiences. Sit for a moment with your arms relaxed, eyes closed, and be aware of how your body feels as a result of your massage. Very slowly begin letting your weight carry you to one side. Gently lean more and more to that side, finally rolling over onto the floor. Stretching out now, lie down on your back and rest. Let the relaxation of your self-massage spread over your body. Allow your breathing to flow easily. If you have trouble relaxing or sleeping, prolong this final phase, or even do it in bed so that you need not get up again and can fall asleep where you are. If you are doing your self-massage to prepare for another activity, get up from the floor by reversing your downward motion: roll onto your side, bend your knees, and push yourself up with your arms, keeping your head and neck relaxed. When you are finally standing, you should feel thoroughly refreshed.

When you become familiar with these different kinds of self-massage, you can incorporate the ones you like best into your daily life. You can find ways to integrate these exercises into your other activities so that your habits and reflexes change and your movements produce relaxation instead. As I mentioned earlier, there are countless other kinds of self-massage which, if you are interested, you can go on to explore. Meanwhile, you can invent new forms of your own as you experiment with those described here.

In the process, you will not only be improving your health and physical appearance but also be increasing your self-knowledge.

EXPERIENCING THE DEEP AND SUBTLE RHYTHMS OF THE BODY

JEFFREY MISHLOVE

Consciousness of psychic and spiritual life is a natural extension of a deep knowing of one's self. This section . . . concerns a process which will gently guide you through the experience of various layers of your own being. You can read each paragraph to yourself and then close your eyes and allow yourself to float into the experiences suggested. Or, you may have a friend who will read this section to you so that you can explore the different levels without interruption. In either case, you will want to be in a comfortable, quiet room where you will not be disturbed for about half an hour.

Become aware of the position you are in and the particular tensions which may exist in your limbs or torso as you are sitting. If you are feeling tense try and loosen the tension somewhat by tightening up that area of the body. Hold it tight for about five or ten seconds and then relax. Do this at least twice for every stiff area.

Be particularly conscious of your shoulders and neck. You can relax the neck by slowly rolling it around on the shoulders to the right in a full circle and then to the left.

Shake the tension out of your arms and legs and hands and feet. Become aware of how you hold your body. Now easily let yourself experience the lightness of your body. It's possible that you may have deeper tensions which you cannot so easily release. Simply be aware of these tensions and assume the most comfortable sitting (or lying down if someone is reading to you) position you can.

Slowly focus on your breathing. Feel the air enter your nostrils and throat. Become aware of the life-giving gases from the atmosphere—which touches all of us—entering into the tiny sacs within your lungs and becoming incorporated into your body through the bloodstream. Become aware of the rhythm of your breathing as your breath flows in and out of your body.

Take a deep breath and hold it for about five seconds. Release the air and let your breath return to normal. Recognize the breath as one of the doorways to higher consciousness. See how easily it passes between the conscious and the subliminal mind.

Tune into your digestive system, starting with your mouth, teeth, tongue and salivary glands. Be aware of your esophagus carrying food into your stomach. Can you feel your stomach and intestines breaking down your last meal into the tiny particles which will be carried into the bloodstream? Feel the smooth muscles gently push the food through your digestive tract. Be aware of the tension, or lack of tension, in your stomach, intestines, and bowels. Let yourself remember the different emotions which you associate with eating, digesting and eliminating food. If there is any residual tightness or tension, just easily observe it for now. Are you feeling hungry or thirsty? Simply let awareness of these deeper levels of your being float through your stream of consciousness.

Become aware of the blood circulating the life-giving breath and food to every cell in your body, cleansing away impurities. Feel the blood flowing from the tip of your feet to the top of your head. Feel it flow through your fingertips. Feel it flow inside your abdomen. Feel the blood flow through your face. Listen to the sound in your ears.

Easily feel your heartbeat, pumping the blood to every cell in your body. Just relax and tune into the rhythm of your own heart. Now feel the rhythms of your heart, lungs, and digestion working together.

As your blood removes the waste products and impurities from every cell in your body, the blood itself is cleansed through the functioning of your kidneys and bladder. Just as the heart and lungs follow a regular rhythm in your life, your urination has a pulse of its own. Become aware of the tension that may or may not exist in your bladder.

Some of your body's waste products are eliminated through the pores of your skin as sweat. Tune into your skin. Feel the touch of your clothing against your body.

Feel the touch of the floor or the chair you are sitting in. How sensitive the skin is. Notice how your skin responds to the moisture or dryness of the room you are in, as well as to the temperature. Softly blow on your skin and feel the air currents. Feel the subtle touch of the sounds of the room you are in against your skin. Notice how different areas of your skin respond with different sensitivities.

Now relax and feel the many rhythms of your body all together. Your muscles. Your breathing. Your digestion. Your heartbeat. Your bladder. Your skin. Feel the billions of cells living and breathing, digesting and dying within your body.

Feel the emotions within your mind and body, the desires and anticipations, the residual feelings of frustration and anger. Feel your own relaxation. Be aware of the ebb and flow of the hormonal tides through your body and your mind. Notice the feelings in your chest area, through your guts, around your genitals, in your throat.

Watch the patterns within your own nervous system. Close your eyes and see the changing forms and colors in your visual field. Observe a train of thought as it emerges and delicately passes through your awareness.

Observe the dream-like forms always dancing in the deeper levels of your mind.

Now relax and feel the many rhythms of your mind and body together. Your breathing, your heartbeat, your digestion, your bowels and bladder, your muscles, your skin, your emotions, the dancing patterns of your nervous system. Allow yourself to breathe gently and be aware of all of these levels within you.

Imagine now the lifespace immediately around your body. Visualize your body's electromagetic field which extends infinitely away in all directions.

Visualize the thought-forms which you generate in this lifespace as a result of your own personality and activities. Give your lifespace its own characteristic colors, shapes, sounds, and smells.

Recollect the rhythm of activity within your lifespace as you go through your day. Remember the states of awareness and the feelings with which you imbue your lifespace. Feel the different pulsebeats of your lifespace: From waking to sleeping and dreaming. From working to relaxing. From month to month. From season to season.

From year to year. From birth to death. Feel the different qualities of living and dying within your lifespace.

Now let your awareness expand out beyond your immediate lifespace to fill up the room or area you are in. Feel the walls and corners and ceiling and floor of the room, and feel yourself within it as well. Be aware of the interaction between your presence and the qualities of the room you are now in.

Gradually imagine your awareness expanding out beyond the room you are in to encompass the entire building and even the surrounding neighborhood. Again feeling the quality of the fluctuation of life, be aware of the plants and animals and people within this space.

Now imagine yourself floating higher and higher above your neighborhood so that you can see for miles around you. Feel the children and the old people, the young lovers and the heartbroken, the wealthy and the needy, the sacred and the profane places. Feel the pulse of life in this space. Feel the earth touch the sky.

Still floating higher you can look down over lakes and rivers, over many towns and cities. Now you can see the great plains and the ocean and feel the slow rhythm of the entire planet turning. Imagine yourself, quite comfortably, floating even higher until you can see the continents beneath you. And there is both day and night. As you rise higher and higher, imagine the civilizations and the spirit of man on this planet.

Rising still higher, visualize the earth as a round turquoise set against the black starry sky. Now look out upon the moon circling the earth approximately every 28 days, changing its phases, exerting a gravitational pull upon the tides of the earth, influencing the minds of poets and lunatics.

Imagine yourself traveling farther out in space now, comfortable, and in the quiet company of others who are taking similar trips in their imagination. Feel the warmth and life-giving energy of the sun. Observe in your imagination solar-storm and solar flare activity, influenced by the electromagnetic and gravitational pull of the planets. Feel yourself bathed in the sun's ionic atmosphere which engulfs the earth and is responsible for the Northern Lights. Feel the life of the solar system interacting with your presence. Behold the planets, symbolic of the ancient gods of man, each following its own cyclical journey through time and space.

As you continue to travel farther and farther into space visualize the solar system growing smaller and smaller until it is just another star somewhat near the edge of the giant galaxy we call the *milky way*. Feel the great spiral of energy in which our own solar system, and many others, are nourished.

Now imagine yourself travelling farther, beyond the galaxy, beyond many other galaxies, farther into the blackness of space until you are at the very edge of the observable universe. Comfortably now moving even farther out into the vast abyss of space feel the absolute essence of the universe which interpenetrates all manifested life. Feel the unchanging calm which underlies all rhythm and fluctuation.

Become aware now of the quiet self within you, beyond all change, which has calmly observed yourself observing yourself, felt yourself feeling yourself, known yourself knowing yourself.

Feel the ultimate nourishment which this transcendental self provides for all of your other movements in life. Allow yourself to stay in this space for several more minutes.

Gradually, when you are ready, begin reentry into your body. As you begin to feel the minute vibrations of light and gravity, pulsing through the universe of your body, remember that the calmness of the transcendental space, beyond the edge of the universe, will always be there for you to return to.

Imagine the vibrations becoming more intense, now forming cloudlike particles which dance and play like the images in your dreams. Gradually whirling atoms and chains of molecules are forming and you can feel the attractions and interactions which are the chemical basis of your very existence.

Now visualize the cells within your body and feel the billions of tiny, living monads, each with its own life-cycle, which constitute your being. Feel the desires and fulfillments of your body on the cellular level. Feel the cells actualizing themselves by forming into tissues and organs. Tune in to the wonderful intelligence within you which organizes this vast kingdom of life.

Now relax and feel the many rhythms of your being all together. Your breathing, your heartbeat, your digestion, the billions of cells living and dying within you, your skin, your emotions, the dancing patterns of your nervous system, your room, your community, nation, planet, feel the pulse of the solar system and of the galaxy. Allow yourself to breathe gently and be aware of all of these levels of your being.

When you are ready, easily get up and move about. Stretch yourself a bit, and with a new understanding of your beingness, continue the activities of your life . . .

PREPARING TO MEDITATE

MICHAEL J. EASTCOTT

Whatever posture we choose, it will be helpful to adopt it in every meditation that we can. Attitudes make associations in the subconscious; lying down is associated with sleeping, for instance, and kneeling with prayer. Therefore, our meditation posture will assume a special meaning in our unconscious and aid our slipping quickly into the right meditative state.

The first deliberate action when we are settled in place is relaxation. The word "deliberate" is worth noting here, because from now on each process that we carry out must be an intended and directed act of the will. True meditation is not a negative sitting back in reverie—as said before, but always to be remembered. It is a positive, carefully directed and quite scientific method of working with the consciousness according to spiritual laws.

For anyone wanting to go fully into the subject of relaxation, there are any amount of books on it and methods taught. But for our purpose, a simple and rapid technique of relaxing all the muscles should be enough; we do not want to devote our meditation time to thought on the physical body for any longer than we need.

We must, however, watch against tension creeping up. Concentration is apt to make us frown—if not clench

hands and teeth! This makes no contribution to the calm
we are seeking and the general pervasion of well-being
which meditation should bring. It may even be harmful,
bringing stress and fatigue. So a short but deliberate relaxing exercise will make a wise beginning, with a moment
of focus on each possible "culprit," from forehead and
eyes, right down to the feet. After a time this will become
an automatic and streamlined proceeding, taking even less
than a minute, but to begin with it is worth some care.

Slowing down the rhythm of the breathing also has a
relaxing effect. A quiet out-breathing while thinking—and
saying aloud if possible—"peace" or any other quietening
word with each letting go of tension, will be found a combined tranquillizing act. The relaxing process is backed up
by the rhythm of the breathing and the effect on the subconscious of words and sound.

As we gradually quieten and lengthen the breathing, the
whole system slows down. Physical relaxing has only been
a preliminary, now we have to calm the emotions and the
mind. But in line with our aim of achieving serenity, the
breathing should never be extended beyond comfort or
held in a way to involve strain. The objective is to establish
a quiet, slow rhythm that will steady the whole system,
giving us freedom to proceed. Extensive breathing exercises should not be undertaken in connection with meditation at this stage. They can hold real danger and beginners
should beware of elaborate methods often used in the East.
They are not wise for the western aspirant.

But, as with relaxation, we can follow a simple method
that will serve to tranquillize physically, emotionally and
mentally, and draw in the attention to a rhythmic
calm. . . .

Technique for Achieving Alignment

The physical body is the house of our feelings and reactions, and with the brain cells we carry out the activity of
the mind. The quiet co-operation of the physical body is
therefore a first essential when we start to meditate. Right
poise and relaxation help to bring this about . . . The following is a simple way to proceed:

1. Having found a comfortable position, make a deliberate effort to relax all physical tension. Think right through

the body from head to foot, relaxing each part. Nervous tension must be consciously released, and after a minute or two we should be still physically poised, but *at rest*.

This is important because any muscles held tense will begin to ache and fidget as time goes on and this will draw back our attention. We need to forget the physical body to pursue our higher intention, so we must see that it is put at ease.

2. The breathing should now be quietened and slowed down. Counting, say five, six, seven, or whatever proves a comfortable rate, while drawing in the breath and again with its exhalation helps to create a rhythm, which has its own quietening effect. Find a count which steadies down the breathing but does not stretch the capacity, or it will be difficult to maintain it and, again, the objective is to establish a quiet *ease*. Newcomers to meditation should never attempt elaborate breathing exercises. They can seriously over-stimulate, which only mitigates against the need for us to become gradually and steadily aligned and attuned.

Once the rhythm is established, stop counting, or it can become a mental habit difficult to break. The breathing must be forgotten once the rhythm is set afoot. A good way of doing this is to use a phrase with the same number of syllables as the count, and if we use appropriate words, this takes us smoothly on to the next stage. For example, if we have been mentally counting six on each in and out breath, the following phrase, again said silently, will be in the same rhythm and at the same time establish the next stage:

"I am at ease and all my feelings are serene."

Any words can be used which embody the stage or quality to be next attained, but no word or phrase should be repeated more than a few times, as if it is continued it may have a hypnotic effect and this is *not* the objective of meditation.

3. Polarization is now on the emotional level. Draw in the consciousness from all reactions and attitudes, drop all antipathies and anticipations, and try to stand in consciousness at a still, central point. This may be helped, again, by framing in words the state being aimed at, saying for example:

"I am a center of calm, clarity and light."

Visualization can also help in creating this still center of consciousness. The emotional body can be imagined and visualized as a smooth and limpid pool, with a quiet, reflective quality which will offer no impediment to alignment with the mind.

If strong emotions are playing in us which make this difficult—a recently aroused anger, for instance, or excitement or high feeling of any kind, a short technique using the symbology of water, which is the symbol of the emotions, can be very helpful. Visualize a stormy sea, with the waves running high, depicting and expressing the strong or turbulent emotion. See this emotion expending itself as the energy in the waves while you visualize them sweeping by and breaking. Then see the whole picture gradually quietening; calm down your sea deliberately until it stretches out to the horizon with only a ripple here and there to show its living responsiveness to the sunlight streaming down.

4. Now raise the consciousness to the mind. Here again the attention must be drawn in from the periphery and from all extraneous thoughts to the center. This central point of focus will be held steady by thought on a particular theme . . . For our present purpose of alignment, a simple phrase like the following can be used:

"I am a point of focussed thoughts."

Have confidence that you now stand as a clear channel, stilled, lighted and prepared to communicate with the Soul, to direct the lower threefold attention, like the beam of a searchlight, toward the area in which that Being dwells.

MEDITATION AS RELAXATION

JEROME ELLISON

(Jerome Ellison, author and educator, founded the Phenix Society, a national association of men and women who seek to improve the quality of their lives through reading, discussion and meditation. This chapter is printed by permission from a forthcoming book, *The Best Is Yet To Be,* which is a manual on how to live radiantly and die wisely. *Editors.*)

A meditation teacher was asked how long a meditation should last. He answered that twenty minutes or so was a good interval. "But," he added, "five minutes that you *do* is better than twenty minutes that you should do but don't." It was good advice. Meditation can relax you—but you have to *do* it. This is an article on doing it. So, with only one brief preliminary remark, let's get down to business.

The preliminary remark is this: Valuable though relaxation is to the often desperately tense person, there are greater rewards in meditation than mere relaxation. These include sharpened mental processes, improved health and interpersonal relations, and for some steadfast souls, enlightenment. However, none of these become available until one has first learned to relax. Relaxation comes first.

We will discuss three pre-meditation relaxation techniques that can be immediately useful to the modern citizen who feels himself to be hard-pressed. The first is the kind of thing you might do, say, once a month, setting aside in advance a sufficient block of time for it so that you can really let yourself get into it and become relaxed as you've never been relaxed before.

The second is for daily use, no matter how busy you think you are, and requires only fifteen to twenty minutes.

The third is something you can do at odd moments during the day—while waiting for a stoplight to change, for a traffic snarl to clear up, or in whatever spare time may come your way.

The longest one is placed first for a reason. It is to plant firmly in your mind some notion of what really deep relaxation can be like, so that when you come back to it (as you will if you really intend to *do* this) your awareness will have had some preparation. The best way to use this chapter, for one who seriously plans to learn relaxation, is the read the whole thing through at a sitting, and then, as time allows, come back to it and actually do it. You will be mildly surprised and greatly pleased at the results.

Now for the infrequent (once a month or so) relaxation method—"the long form." When you get around to actually doing this, you'll want to fold your book back so it stays open, and crease these instruction pages so they turn easily. When you first read the instructions through to get the general idea, you'll be wide awake and alert. When you get around to using them, there will be times when you'll be in a lazy drowse that's close to the dream-state. It will not be necessary to memorize this sequence. In this state you'll be glancing at the book just long enough to pick up the clue on what you do next. You will keep minimal attention on the book, maximum attention on relaxing your body. This brief interruption to glance at the next instruction will not hamper your relaxation. You will return to you procedures and gain their full benefit. If you can imagine yourself, instead of reading the next step, just *dreaming* of reading it, you've hit the right note.

These are the directions for infrequent deep relaxation:

1. Arrange to be in a place where you can be entirely by yourself for several hours, a place that is quiet.

2. Free your body from any binding. If your shoes bind, kick them off. If belt, collar or bra feel tight, loosen them.

3. Get some circulation going. If you have your own regular setting-up exercises, do them--for not more than five minutes. If not, do these (but for not more than five minutes): Bend forward and reach toward your toes several times (don't strain to touch toes if it doesn't come easily). Hold your arms straight out from your shoulders and turn head and trunk to the left as far as they will *com-*

fortably go, looking as far to the rear as you can without straining. Swing and do the same thing to the right. Repeat four times. Do four squats and four pushups.

4. Seat yourself comfortably in a chair that provides full support for back and head. Legs uncrossed, feet on the floor.

5. Take four of the kind of deep breaths called complete "yoga-breaths,"* breathing in until the lower chest is filled with air, the downward thrust of the diaphragm forcing the abdomen out, then filling the upper chest as full as you can with air, then exhaling. Do this four times.

6. Close your eyes and relax into your chair. Imagine a small bottle of a warm, fragrant lotion marked "relaxation" being unstoppered and poured over the top of your head. A pleasant, warm, relaxing sensation now begins to spread down over the scalp, over the forehead, back of the ears, down the neck and shoulders, over the face. Muscles of the face, neck and tongue relax as the feeling descends.

7. Close your eyes as tightly as you can. (Except for glancing at these directions, your eyes will remain closed throughout, but right now you're holding them *tightly* closed.) After a few seconds, release the eyelid strain and let your closed eyelids completely relax.

8. Pull in all your face muscles toward the tip of your nose, scrunching them in as tight as you can. (Never mind how silly you look, no one is watching). Now relax the whole facial muscular system completely. Take a deep yoga-breath.

9. Pull up the corners of your mouth into a great big silly circus-clown grin, dragging each corner toward the cheekbone as far as it will go. Hold it for a few seconds. Let it go. Take a deep breath.

10. Now tense up the whole hand-arm-shoulder-chest muscular system as hard and tense as you can make it. Starting from each fist tightly clenched into a hard ball, strain the muscles of the forearm, then upper arm—biceps against triceps—then tighten the shoulder muscles (deltoids), then the same for the chest muscles (pectorals) all very tight. Do the whole muscle system right across,

*See page 142 for a full description. *Editors*.

fist to fist, tense and tight. Hold this for a few seconds. Now relax the whole system completely, all at once. Take a deep breath.

11. Rest for a few seconds.

12. Pull your abdominal muscles as far back toward your spine as possible, straining hard as you can. Hold them in a few seconds, then let them go, totally and all at once. Take a deep breath.

13. Now tighten up the whole muscular system from the toes through the buttocks—straining the muscles of the calves, of the thighs, drawing the toes into a tight curl, firming up the buttocks good and hard, each muscle straining against its opposite throughout the whole system, very, very taut. Now relax the whole system entirely, letting it go all at once. Take a deep breath.

14. Turn the feet outward, splay-foot, as far as they'll go, forcing them, holding them splay-foot for a few seconds. Now turn them inward, pigeon-toed, as far as they'll go, and hold a few seconds. Center the feet and relax them totally. Take a deep breath.

15. You are now in a deep state of relaxation. Remain there for a few seconds, deeply, totally relaxed.

16. Now you will go still deeper. Imagine yourself descending on an escalator to the fifth level below ground. Count one floor at a time, for five floors, at each floor going into a deeper state of relaxation. From ground floor where you start, board the escalator and let yourself drift gently down to level one. Turn, take the next down-escalator and float softly down to level two. Take the next down-escalator to level three. Then, taking your time, board the down-escalator and flow down to level four. Then, ever so easily, down to the deepest—level five.

17. You are now in a very deep state of relaxation. Tell yourself that you will remain there as long as you like. Just as long as you like. When you choose to return to normal awareness, tell yourself you will do so gradually. Not suddenly, but gradually, at the slow count of five. But there's no hurry about this. Remain relaxed as long as you like, until you feel entirely rested.

18. At a long count of five, imagine yourself ascending the escalators to ground level, one floor for each count, slowly rising to the surface—one going up, two going up, three going up. Pause at four, and tell yourself that

at five you will be in full normal waking consciousness, feeling immeasurably refreshed and buoyed by a beautiful lightness. Before going on to five, open your eyes half way, blink them once or twice, close them again. Taking your time, take the up-escalator for the count five. You are now wide awake, fully refreshed, feeling finer than you've felt in years. *Remember this feeling.* If you fix it well in memory, you will be able to return to this depth of relaxation in the future in a matter of seconds, when your available time does not allow all the preliminaries. If you're really after relaxation, however, this "long-form" should be repeated about once a month, for maintenance. You can also use it for occasions when you're *really* uptight—that is to say, *beside* yourself—emergency occasions when you need relaxation more than you need anything else and can therefore afford to give it first priority.

Now let us consider normal, daily, brief relaxation. This is the kind described in the introduction to this article as "the second technique—for daily use, no matter how busy you think you are—requires only twenty minutes." This is tailored for the hectic hurly-burly of daily urban living. It goes like this:

The first step is to bring to mind something that for *you* symbolizes or stands as something closely connected with. The Infinite. If you are religious, you may choose a religious symbol of some kind. Francis Geddes, who is religious, describes his imagery as follows:

I visualize myself sitting in the center of an inner sanctuary, circular in design, whose ceiling is a round glass dome above me to admit the light. I then seek to become completely silent and still. My surface consciousness, however, has a lot of *thoughts* that it keeps popping into my mind. I look at the thoughts and acknowledge them. Some I agree to come back to and work on after meditation, but *all* thoughts are briefly acknowledged and then placed outside the sanctuary. It may take five or six minutes, with a parade of many thoughts before my sanctuary becomes quiet enough for the stillness to settle around me. This stillness takes the place of the many intruding thoughts.

If you are not religious, you may choose to draw your imagery from nature. In creating your image, only two things matter: (1) it must be an image of peace and quiet and (2) it must have some connection with The Infinite. For many, the image of a quiet, beautiful lake nestled in a remote, deserted mountain valley serves both purposes very well. It is quiet and peaceful. It reflects the brilliant, distant sun by day and the immeasurably distant stars by night, and is therefore a reflection of the tangible infinite.

Some like to think of themselves as immersed in a clear pool, where bubbles coming up from a spring at the bottom keep disturbing the stillness. Each bubble is a thought. To still the thoughts—which is the object of relaxation—they dive down trying to arrest each bubble before it forms, substituting a *mantra* (a silently-repeated meditation word, explained below) for the emerging thought. Thus they dispose of their thoughts one by one, progressing downward toward the clear, peaceful, silent well which is the source of the spring.

Others use water imagery in the form of a river. They are traveling upstream (their "boat" is their mantra) toward its beautiful, peaceful source. Thoughts are people on the shore constantly beckoning to them to come and do this or that. They look down at these thoughts with kindly tolerances—and continue serenely on their mantra-repeating journey. Before you are ready to undertake the second, or daily-routine brief technique, you must settle on one of these, or invent an imagery of your own that fills the bill of peacefulness and connection with the infinite.

Next, you must have a "mantra" or word to repeat to bring your mind to peaceful relaxation. My favorite is the traditional mantra "Om" (pronounced "ohm"), and I recommend it. This word, or whatever you choose in its place—such as "One" or "Thine"—repeated over and over silently throughout your meditation is your "mantra." (When thoughts interrupt this repetition, simply put them patiently aside and return to repeating the word.)

Now you are ready to begin. All the following steps can be taken, and enjoyed with benefit, in five to twenty minutes. If you are a beginner, it may be well to start out with ten minutes and gradually stretch it to twenty.

One preliminary admonition: this sequence works best when you do it the first thing in the morning, and that

means the *first* thing—*before* you turn on the news and
before you get into the morning hassle over making the
coffee. Remember, coffee is a stimulant, not a relaxer, and
the morning "news" is deliberately compiled by well-paid
merchants of panic whose sole job is to rile you, alarm
you, scare you and generally unsettle you with whatever
scare-stuff they may have on hand. Don't fall for it. The
news can wait until *after* your relaxation, and so can your
coffee, once you get used to this slight change in routine
(it may take a little planning at first).

The procedure:

1. Find a comfortable chair in a quiet place. Don't say,
"In *my* house, that's impossible." It's possible in practically
all houses, though it may mean getting up half an hour
before anybody else does.

2. Sit in the chair. Your back should be reasonably
straight though not ramrod stiff. Hands may be in the lap
or on the arms of the chair; feet on the floor. Clothing
should be arranged so that nothing binds.

3. Take four deep yoga breaths as described earlier.

4. Close your eyes and visualize as clearly as you can
whatever symbol or scene of peace-and-quiet-associated-
with-the-infinite you have chosen.

5. Start repeating your mantra-word at your own speed,
consciously relaxing your body as you do so. By this
I mean calling to mind the deep state of relaxation you
were in the last time you did the "long-form" relaxation
previously described.

6. Tell yourself how many minutes you intend to meditate. It will surprise you to discover quickly that you have
a dependable internal alarm clock that will let you know
when your allowed time is up. If you don't yet trust this, by
all means set your alarm. Get rid of it, however, as soon
as you have won confidence in your inner timekeeper.

7. Continue repeating your mantra. When thoughts interrupt, set them aside with kindliness and return to your
mantra. This gentleness in putting thoughts aside is important. If you let yourself get sore—either at the thoughts
for interrupting, or at yourself for allowing them to—you
have defeated your purpose, since an angry person cannot
be a relaxed one, and our goal here is relaxation. Flora
Davis, in describing her meditation experiences has put
the case well: "When I closed my eyes, the first thing I

noticed was a kind of rosy-orange color. Then I became conscious of what it means to concentrate on the repetition of a single word. My mind kept leaping off on tangents. Even when I managed to focus on the word briefly, thoughts kept trickling in around it. The mind is apparently perfectly capable of chanting a word while simultaneously worrying away at some problem. After ten minutes the phone rang. I dealt with the phone call, then went back to finish my twenty-minute stint—gladly. The peripheral thoughts began to slow down. At the end, I felt unusually relaxed."

You, too, will feel unusually relaxed if you follow this method—and persevere. Perseverance is vital. A young lady meditator once said to Swami Muktananda: "Swami, I've been sitting and meditating for weeks, and nothing happens. What should I do?" The Swami replied, "Lie down and meditate," with the implication, but *meditate*. Maharishi Mahesh Yogi, founder of the TM® movement, repeatedly tells his followers, "There is no such thing as an unsuccessful meditation." Every reasoned, sincere effort to gain inner calm, by following the directions of those who have experienced it, has an accumulating beneficial effect. Though surface evidence of this effect may not be instantly apparent, it beautifully reveals itself when given a little time. Bear constantly in mind the little tip that opened this article: "Five minutes that you *do* is better than twenty minutes that you should do but don't."

The "five minutes" is to be taken quite literally—distinct benefits can be had from relaxations as brief as one or two minutes. This brings us to technique number three of the triad announced at the beginning as "something you can do at odd moments during the day." Instead of fussing and fuming at life's petty delays—waiting for the dentist to see you, or for the "walk" sign to let you cross a street, or for a package to be wrapped, or for your lunch to be served—you can gain both inner and outer serenity by using these brief intervals to meditate. You might even, as Dr. Herbert Benson has suggested, take a relaxation-break instead of a coffee-break. Caffeine, a nerve and heart stimulant, tends to make you tense and jittery. Meditation relaxes. So relax.

The technique here requires a little experience (though surprisingly little) in the first two methods, and is based on this experience. With a trial run of techniques one and two under your belt, you're ready for a go at the quickie-method, number three.

The procedure:

1. Call instantly to mind your chosen image of a symbol or scene that is sublimely peaceful and related to the infinite. Dwell on this for a few seconds—long enough to fix it firmly in your mind. Then, without letting go of this image entirely, let it fade into the background while you proceed to—

2. Remember as vividly as you can how you felt the last time you got yourself deeply relaxed by following "long form" relaxation as in Procedure One. Give yourself over entirely to these two things—relaxing the mind into the image of peace and infinity, relaxing the body into the recollection of its last deep relaxation. If your snippet of time is not yet used up, you can go on to—

3. Start up your mantra, keeping intruding thoughts out of the scene by one of the methods given you in this chapter.

I'm giving our closing passage to a quote from Flora Davis on a theme whose importance cannot be overemphasized in all undertakings bearing on relaxation and meditation. That theme is "easy does it." The moment you begin to get anxious, tense or impatient, or to strain for results, or to curse yourself because you failed to keep all stray thoughts out of your adventure into peace, you have lost the ball game—because, of course, these feelings are the opposites of relaxation.

Easy does it.

"Effort," Flora Davis writes, "is what keeps you from reaching the restful depths of the mind. This made me realize, at one point, that I had fallen into the trap of judging each meditation by how well I stayed with the mantra. I'd become annoyed with myself for drifting— even though I knew that annoyance made me tense and counter-productive."

Perseverance, yes. Effort, beyond a calm assertion of your own will over your own mind and body, no.

Easy does it.

RELAXATION THROUGH YOGA

SWAMI KARMANANDA (MICHAEL VOLIN)

(Swami Karmananda studied yoga in China, Tibet and India with Hindu, Buddhist and Taoist masters. He has written ten books on yoga, and teaches in the New York City area. He can be contacted at the Michael Volin School of Yoga, 103 Gedney Street, Nyack, NY 10960. *Editors.*)

According to an ancient legend, a king once asked a wise old yogi, "What is happiness?" The sage whispered into the king's ear only one word: "Peace."

The answer to real happiness is indeed a state of inner tranquility and balance. You cannot be happy when torn apart by inner conflicts or when your mind is preoccupied by problems and worries. Happiness is inner peace—perfect harmony within.

According to yoga philosophy, we accumulate tension from at least the age of puberty—most likely well before that. This has been known for thousands of years. Early sages of yoga philosophy discussed the subject at length and created a number of exercises to deal with this problem. An ancient essay on tension describes it as a "vampire," a monster that lives within the body and gorges itself on a person's life force.

Modern psychiatrists agree with this suggestion, saying that continuous tension is the major cause of many maladies, including premature aging. It has been known to medical science for a long time that those with excellent health and longevity are among the most placid and mentally well-balanced people. "Do not let any emotions penetrate more than skin deep," says an old proverb, suggesting that you not become upset, whatever the circumstances. In yogic training, tranquility and balance, inner calmness and peace are among the most important attainments.

This ancient belief has been confirmed by science often. Most recently, an article appeared in *The New York Times* (30 November 1975) entitled "India Evaluating Effects of Yoga," which carried the subhead "Researchers Find Practice Relieves Stress Diseases." The article told of a team of doctors and researchers at Benares Hindu University in Benares, backed by both the university and Indian government, which reported that it has established, after a three-year study, that "yoga and meditation could provide relief from a variety of stress diseases that afflict people in industrial nations. Such illnesses include high blood pressure, heart attack, peptic ulcer, insomnia and drug addiction." The researchers said that they had also found subjects to have heightened virility and a slowdown in aging processes due to yoga exercises.

Dr. K. N. Udupa, head of the research team, said that six months of systematic training in yogic exercises produced several beneficial effects. The subjects shed weight; appetites improved; respiratory problems, nervous tension and mental excitement disappeared; high blood pressure and cholesterol dropped to normal levels; and addiction to drugs, pills and alcohol gradually disappeared. "Having established this," Dr. Udupa remarked, "I would certainly recommend yoga therapy for all mental and psychosomatic ailments."

It is fine for science to validate the claims of yoga in the realm of physiology. But there is more to yoga than this. It is primarily a means of attaining the highest state of consciousness, which is the meaning of the word "yoga." This state of supreme bliss can never be achieved until your inner life has been brought into complete harmony and balance. Likewise in the art of delaying aging, inner tranquility plays an important role. One who masters inner tension traditionally conquers the passage of time.

Problems related to stress and tension are far too serious and widespread in modern society to be dealt with lightly. Yoga offers many techniques to combat inner tension by dealing with a person on all levels of being—physical, mental and spiritual. Its ancient wisdom can help our world overcome this crucial situation.

Breath control plays a very important part in yoga. The physiology of breathing must be understood by a student of yoga, along with the esoteric teachings connected with it, and the full abdominal breath of a yogi must be mastered.

The right instrument for breathing is the nose. This is the way animals breathe, and animals are masters of the art of relaxation. Yoga teaches that breathing through the nose controls the flow of *prana,* the cosmic life force, into the body. The ancient yogis discovered that a person's breathing varies during the day from nostril to nostril. At times the breath flows more freely through the right nostril than the left, and then every few hours the dominance pattern will shift.

Inhaled through the nose according to esoteric teachings, prana first makes contact with the Ida and Pingala *nadis* in the nostrils. Nadis are translated from yogic physiology as nerves. Ida and Pingala are described in yogic anatomy as tubes that originate at the base of the spine, crossing and recrossing the spinal column as they rise to the brain, ending in the left and right nostril respectively. Modern physiologists suggest that these terms refer to the gangliated cords of the sympathetic nervous system on each side of the spine.

Ida and Pingala also branch into the upper layer of the brain, the cortex, suggesting a connection between brain functioning and breathing. This seems sensible when you consider that the brain, which weighs about three pounds, nevertheless consumes about one-fifth of all oxygen taken into the body. It is also interesting to note that the emblem of medicine—the caduceus or wand of Mercury, symbol of healing—is derived from a traditional drawing of the spinal column and its ancillary nerve cords.

Mouth breathing is a typical trait of retardation. This is obvious in the stereotype of the slack-jawed "village idiot." Some types of mental retardation can be traced to mouth breathing. The upper layer of the child's brain never was properly stimulated through nostril breathing. Certain branches of yoga—namely, raja yoga and kundalini yoga—teach that we use only a small fraction of our mental potential and that the remainder can be developed by special breathing exercises.

On the other hand, anger, jealousy, grief, hatred, frustration and all other destructive emotions can be controlled by proper breathing. Even simple nervousness, shyness and "stage fright" will respond to the change of vibrations

brought about by slowing down the rhythm of the breath.
As the heart slows in response to the reduced breathing rate,
the agitation, nervousness and tension will gradually decrease.

Most people are literally "uptight" and do not know
how to breathe properly. Observe someone—yourself first
—and you will probably see that he breathes with his
chest only in short, shallow breaths. This thoracic breathing—breathing that involves only the thorax—is indicative of deep, unrecognized tension. It is detrimental to
health because it retains stale, used air in the lungs. This
is a long way from the free, easy way that a baby breathes.
Baby breathing is abdominal breathing, belly breathing.
So is animal breathing. This is proper breathing.

The complete yoga breath involves use of the abdomen
and diaphragm, and restores natural breathing. It permits
the lungs to be completely filled with each inhalation and
emptied with each exhalation, reducing the amount of
residual air to a minimum. The technique of retaining the
inhaled breath gives maximum opportunity for the incom-
ing fresh air to purify the bloodstream, but I will not discuss that here.

To begin this exercise, lie down on the floor. Place your
hands lightly on your abdomen just below the navel, with
fingertips touching. Inhale through the nose and at the
same time let the abdomen swell out. Make a conscious
effort to extend the abdomen as if your were developing a
"pot belly." The fingertips should move apart as the abdomen swells out.

Then exhale through the nose, and at the same time
draw in the stomach so that your fingertips come together
again. Make a conscious effort to "suck in the gut"
slightly.

As the abdomen rises with inhalation, the diaphragm
moves downward and the bottom of the lungs start to
fill with air. As the breath continues, the lower part of
the chest is expanded and the lungs further filled. Finally,
the upper ribs are expanded and slightly lifted so that the
tops of the lungs are filled. Inhalation is now complete, and
you should feel that your entire torso from hips to neck
is filled with air.

The process is reversed in exhalation. As you release the

breath, the drawn-in stomach lifts the diaphragm and begins to empty the lungs. Then the expanded ribs relax to a
normal position, and the exhalation is completed.

Thus described, the breath is in three stages, but in
practice it becomes one smooth, continuous and effortless
movement. You should practice these movements until they
are familiar enough to be performed without conscious
direction. It may help to visualize the trunk of the body
as a glass of water being filled and emptied. During inhalation, imagine the air to be water being poured into a
glass. Just as a glass is filled from the bottom up, so will
the body be filled with air, starting from below the navel
and rising to the very top of the lungs. During exhalation,
as the glass is emptied, air leaves the body from the top
first and then the middle until the last "drop" is "poured"
out from the bottom of the abdomen.

In breath control we have to consider four movements:
inhalation, exhalation, retention of breath and retention of
emptiness. Physiology of breathing teaches that each of
these movements produces certain physiological phenomena. With inhalation, blood pressure rises slightly and
arteries leading to the heart narrow. With exhalation, the
process is reversed; blood pressure goes down and arteries
expand. Retention of breath and retention of emptiness
emphasizes this condition respectively.

We know that breathing oxygenates or purifies our
bloodstream. Yogic physiology maintains that in addition
the entire nervous system is nourished and toned up by
prana in the air. If the first principle in combating tension
is slowing down the rhythm of the breath from a normal
15-20 breaths per minute to only five or six, the second
principle is regulating the rhythm of each respiration cycle
so that inhalation and exhalation are timed to near-perfect
evenness.

A very simple exercise will quickly prove this to anyone.
Sit in a comfortable position, cross-legged on the floor or
semi-reclining in an easy chair. Place your thumb on the
inside of the opposite wrist with your fingers on the outside of the wrist, just as a doctor does when he takes your
pulse. When you have found your pulse, breathe in for a
count of six pulse beats and then breathe out for the same
count. Now close your eyes and focus your attention on

breathing, using your pulse to time inhalation and exhalation. In less than three minutes a sensation of peace and tranquility will be experienced.

Another method of mental and physical pacification is the combination of rhythmical breath and concentration on beautiful, peaceful scenery. Visualize a scene—perhaps one you've actually viewed. After taking a comfortable position and establishing rhythmical breath, concentrate on the image of your natural scene. Hold it firmly in your mind during the exercise. Usually 15-20 minutes is sufficient to produce the desirable result.

In yogic practices often confined to remote ashrams, or monasteries, the power of the "mind's eye" is continuously developed. It plays an important role in many techniques, including some forms of meditation, contemplation and relaxation. "Mind's eye" is predominantly an ability of the human mind to look into the past. It is an ability to see clearly, for example, the face of a friend one hasn't seen for years or a house which was lived in during the past. In yogic training, "mind's eye" is also an ability to look into your inner self in search for possible tension or gaining a better awareness of the mystery of the inner self. This faculty of the human makeup can be considerably improved during the process of training and is very important in gaining mastery over tension.

The famous yogic position called Savasana or "pose of complete rest" is perhaps the most powerful method for overcoming tension. Many scientific studies attest to its dramatic effects in producing deep rest by reducing heart rate, respiration rate and body metabolism in general.

Savasana is practiced in a prone position, either on a bed or on the floor. Minimize disturbances by asking people to leave you alone for half an hour. If there is a telephone in the room, remove the receiver from the cradle. Reduce noise as much as possible and dim the lighting.

Savasana has four stages. In the first, the muscles of the body are completely relaxed, starting from the tip of our toes. Consciously tell the parts of your body to relax, and command them in this order: feet, ankles, calves, knees, thighs, hips, abdominal muscles, buttocks, small of the back, chest, shoulders, arms and hands.

Then continue upward, paying particular attention to the muscles of the face. Notice any tension around the mouth, between the eyebrows, and in the forehead. Relax everything completely. A sensation of pleasant heaviness should be experienced, as if the body is continuously sinking through the floor.

In the second part of the exercise, your mind's eye ability again slowly scans the body in the process of withdrawing inner tension. The power of the mind's eye to look into the body is fully exercised, along with an additional effort of will and concentration, enabling one to achieve total relaxation. Traditionally, this stage is described as relaxation of nervous centers and emptying of the nadis.

Upon achieving this stage, which is more difficult than the first one, deep and rhythmical breath is established. Then you enter the third or recharging stage of the Savasana exercise. Form a mental image of prana (cosmic life force) entering your system with each inhalation. Direct it to every cell of your body. Then as you exhale, visualize the breath purifying and invigorating every cell. Do this for about 30 complete breaths.

The final stage is known as the "small exit from the physical body." You detach yourself from your present environment, including all its problems and worries, and project yourself thousands of miles away into a different world of peace, beauty and serenity. Traditionally this world is a garden, spiritual ashram or retreat created by the imagination. Only ten or fifteen minutes of this exercise, if practiced twice daily, will provide a complete relaxation on the physical, mental and spiritual levels. This technique has been taken over by various mind control courses in a simplistic way and made into one of the key elements in their program.

Many students of yoga reported remarkable results through practice of this exercise. One student, an Englishman and a devoted member of my yoga school in Shanghai, China before World War II, claimed that it saved his life. He was a prisoner in Burma and survived the infamous Burma Road where many thousands of people lost their lives through hardship, malnutrition and disease. Prisoners engaged in building the road had only half an hour's break during a long, strenuous day. The student remembered the exercise and trained himself to lie down perfectly motionless in the shade of some trees for fifteen or twenty minutes during the break. After the war ended, he told me, "I managed not only to relax and restore my physical energy during this time, but for a few minutes I was more in England than in Burma. My body temperature dropped. The smells and sounds of the jungle ceased to exist. I was breathing the cool air of the English country-side and my ears were filled with the soft rustle of garden shrubbery."

This ability to move into a different "dimension"—the spiritual world of your personal garden-retreat—accounts for the near-total absence of nervous breakdown and men-tal disorders in many Eastern countries, including India and China. It is not a way of escaping responsibilities, like an ostrich putting his head in the sand. Rather, this is a powerful method for combating stress and mental pres-sure.

Another famous technique of relaxation is Yoga Nidra or "The Sleepless Sleep of a Yogi." It is based on breath control and concentration. This exercise has a number of variations, but the following method can be easily mastered by the Western student. It is also practiced in a prone position in quiet surroundings, with the possibility of being disturbed minimized.

As in the pose of Savasana, your body is brought into a state of total relaxation, with deep and rhythmical breath established. You gradually detach yourself from the sen-sation of the gross body. Then, mobilizing your imagina-tion to its full extent, think that your body is becoming invisible. It is slowly merging into the air. Next, concen-trate your awareness on the movements of breath. Identify with it and become one with it. A wonderful sensation of lightness and bodilessness will be experienced, leading to a most profound physical and mental relaxation. The sensa-tion is not unlike that during the moments preceding deep sleep when the entire body is completely relaxed. This state is known as "the essence of rest" and it is claimed that a few minutes of fully-achieved Yoga Nidra is equiva-lent to hours of sleep.

The contemplative and meditative practices of raja yoga, as well as a number of mental exercises, are also designed for total relaxation. Purification of the mind leading to mental balance is practiced on a regular basis. This exer-cise is designed to develop positive, constructive thinking and to banish negative thoughts. A subtle mental impulse is the origin of conscious thought. Yoga calls it "the seed of thought," and our minds are full of these seeds, both positive and negative.

Sitting cross-legged in complete stillness of body, with proper breathing established, analyze yourself in deep meditation. Learn to "sort the seeds," to distinguish the subtle mental impulses underlying thought. Fertilize the positive impulses and destroy the negative. You should practice this regularly like a wise gardener returning daily to his garden, watering plants and flowers while destroying weeds. This is how a yogi brings body and mind under complete and conscious control.

Fears, whether conscious or unconscious, are always a source of inner tension. A meditative practice known as "Conquering the Seven Fears" is a powerful tool for combating this. The fears are listed below. Fears are based on ego-attachments. Take each fear in turn and try to develop a positive, constructive attitude toward it. Bear in mind that the hardest battles are fought in the mind, and that life purified of fear is happy and tranquil, free from stress and suffering because all ego-attachments have been conquered.

1. *Fear of losing possessions.* Concentrate on the thought that all material possessions are ephemeral, whereas an awakened spirit is of everlasting value because the spirit is eternal.

2. *Fear of losing health.* A true yogi does his best to maintain good health through diet, ethical restrictions, physical exercises and cultivation of the mind. But if illness comes, the yogi accepts it philosophically as an opportunity to learn and grow still more, while doing what he can to combat it.

3. *Fear of losing friends.* Concentrate on the thought that true friendship cannot be destroyed by physical separation.

4. *Fear of loneliness.* The yogi knows that when he is alone, he is with God Himself. This thought banishes all fear of loneliness.

5. *Fear of losing love.* Love is the strongest force in the universe. It is the light of God; it cannot be destroyed. Concentration on this thought conquers fear of losing love, while discriminating divine love from ego-clinging and immature attachments.

6. *Fear of death.* The last half of every thinking person's life should be a spiritual preparation for death. Yoga philosophy does not consider death as the complete extermination of an individual. It teaches that the spirit is immortal. We are all passing through cycles of incarnations, and the yogi's whole life is an attempt to prepare wisely for those incarnations, to achieve a further stage of development. Acceptance of this gives complete freedom from fear of death and brings a noble serenity in the face of the final liberation of the spirit.

7. *Fear of fear.* Shut your eyes and concentrate on the thought "I am stronger than fear." Think of it as a form of slavery and resolve to free yourself. Think of fear as a weakness and determine to overcome it. Think of it as degrading and humiliating and decide that you will regain your dignity and pride. List all your fears, mental and physical, and analyze each one constructively, trying to see what you can do to eradicate it. Form the habit of thinking in opposites. Whenever the thought of fear—in the abstract—comes to your mind, replace it with the thought of courage. Do this not only while sitting at your exercises, but during your daily life. Use the power of autosuggestion to train yourself into freedom and strength.

Transcendental meditation, so popular nowadays in America, is basically a method to overcome inner tension. As practiced by most people, it is a technique for attaining profound physical and mental relaxation. There is no doubt that it is beneficial in this regard.

But from the point of view of yoga philosophy, it is only one meditational technique of many for entering a higher plane of consciousness. Yoga philosophy aims at complete development of a person—physically, mentally and spiritually—through an integrated, total program of proper nutrition, exercise, mental culture and ethical observances relating to daily life. With regular practice a more healthy attitude toward life and death is achieved by the student of yoga, which leads him in a balanced manner to perfect peace and harmony.

IV
RELAXATION AND PSYCHOTHERAPY

What is without periods of rest will not endure.

Ovid, Heroides

Self-treatment may not be sufficient for severe relaxation-related problems. Such cases will require professional help. This section is therefore intended primarily for the psychotherapeutic community. But the articles have been selected for general readability, and we feel that they will be of interest to the layperson as well as the trained therapist and technician because they present various approaches to the treatment of stress. The Appendix which follows likewise is of greatest use to the professional, but nevertheless is a major resource for the interested reader who wants to explore further in a particular topic.

The reason that medicine and psychotherapy have been concerned with relaxation is succinctly stated by Dr. T. X. Barber, a researcher in hypnotism and altered states of consciousness: "An important fact that has been emphasized by behavior therapists is that anxiety and tension are incompatible with physical and mental relaxation. If a person lets himself relax, he can control or block the anxiety, tension or fear."

Dr. Edmund Jacobson, in his Preface to the second edition of his classic 1928 work *Progressive Relaxation,* observed that medicine has tended to treat the patient more or less as "a mere assembly of organs and tissues." It has studied these assemblies in response to the environment and to disease, chemicals and surgical intervention. But somehow the most important aspect got overlooked in the process—the recognition that a human "is all this and something more, namely, an active individual, autonomously regulating his own actions and in consequence subject to disorders in his functions as active agent."

Dr. Jacobson's research led him to make this statement in the Preface:

On rational grounds no less than on the basis of current physiological knowledge, it seems permissible to say that *to be excited and to be fully relaxed are physiological opposites*. Both states cannot exist in the same locality at the same time. The rule or law thus stated would seem to apply to many conditions familiar in medical practice and would suggest that the role of applied relaxation might be directly efficient.

Today there is a broad spectrum of body therapies aimed at intervening in the self-taught but improper responses people develop that lead to physical and mental malfunctioning. Some are ancient systems such as yoga, tai ch'i chuan and aikido. Others are modern systems, including bioenergetics, structural integration (Rolfing), polarity therapy, the Alexander and Feldenkrais methods, massage of various sorts, autogenic training, progressive relaxation, movement and dance therapy, applied kinesiology and the newest approach, biofeedback.

Dr. Elmer Green has summarized research findings from these systems in the form of a theoretical concept which he calls the "psychophysiological principle." It states: "Every change in the physiological state is accompanied by an appropriate change in the mental-emotional state, conscious or unconscious, and conversely, every change in the mental-emotional state, conscious or unconscious, is accompanied by an appropriate change in the physiological state." In other words, he says, we inhabit a mind-body complex that is interlocked as the warp and woof of a whole piece of cloth.

This principle is both an extension and a refinement of Jacobson's statement, and the applications are dramatic indeed. As the following articles demonstrate, the induction of physical relaxation can lead to decreased mental anxiety that underlies such a large number of illnesses. A list of examples is given by Dr. Barber in *The American Journal of Clinical Hypnosis* (July 1975):

. . . many individuals become tense or anxious when they meet new people, when they are in a strange or new situation, and when they feel that they are being judged by others. Also, individuals who are alcoholics, or who are obese, or who cannot quit smoking become tense and anxious when they have not had alcohol or food or a cigarette for a period of time. Some individuals also have specific kinds of fears; for instance, fear of riding in an airplane, fear of heights, or fear of narrow spaces.

By helping a patient to relax and become aware of his feelings and behavior, he learns to remain calm in otherwise anxious situations. Thus he consciously controls what was previously unconscious and uncontrolled.

Perhaps the most dramatic application of relaxation is being made by Dr. Carl Simonton of Fort Worth, Texas, where he specializes in the treatment of cancer, with notable success. Dr. Simonton is a radiation therapist who has combined his traditional training with new approaches to cancer treatment, including chemotherapy, psychotherapy and a meditation-like visualization procedure coupled with relaxation. He recently described his approach in *The Journal of Transpersonal Psychology* (No. 1, 1975):

> During the first week a patient comes to our office, he attends what we call an orientation session [with his family]. During the orientation session, we explain our concept of disease, how the mind interacts with the body and how attitude plays a major role. We teach our patients a technique which we call relaxation and visualization. You might call it biofeedback without a machine, meditation, autogenic training. There are lots of names for it, but it is a basic relaxation technique in which the patients are told to visualize their disease, their treatment and their body's own immune mechanisms (we call them white blood cells to make it simple), acting on that disease. We tell them to do this three times a day, every day.

This visualization-relaxation procedure is a key element in Dr. Simonton's treatment, and for a surprisingly large number of his patients, it works.

The following articles make two important points. First, they show the layperson that help *is* available for even the most difficult sort of stress-induced problems. Second, they show the trained professional that a wide variety of approaches are being explored by competent researchers, whose results should be most heartening to both patient and therapist.

We are especially pleased to be able to present a summary of the research done at Harvard University by Richard J. Davidson and Dr. Gary E. Schwartz. Their exploration of the different modes of anxiety, showing that some therapies are better for *cognitive* tension while others are suited to *somatic* tension, is an important conceptual breakthrough for the diagnosis and treatment of relaxation-related problems.

ANXIETY REDUCTION THROUGH SELF-ADMINISTERED RELAXATION

HAROLD H. DAWLEY, JR.

The therapeutic potential of self-administered behavioral techniques is slowly being realized. Dawley, Floyd, and Smith (2) reviewed 37 studies pertaining to self-administered, minimal therapist contact, and automated behavior therapy and concluded that available research clearly indicates that behavioral procedures can successfully be self-administered. Several books (7, 10-12) are oriented toward self-directed behavior therapy. One of the first studies of self-administered behavior therapy was reported by Migler and Wolpe (8). In their study, the patient recorded his own relaxation instructions and successfully carried out his own desensitization at home.

Relaxation training is an integral part of many behavioral procedures and, as such, can also be self-administered. Denholtz (3) reported the successful use of tape-recorded relaxation instructions between treatment sessions to enhance therapeutic effectiveness. Allen found self-administered relaxation and study counseling as effective as group relaxation and study counseling (therapist present) in the reduction of test anxiety.

The average patient spends a large amount of time which is not utilized therapeutically. This is true for the psychiatric as well as the medical patient. Self-administered behavior therapy (relaxation in particular) offers potential for expanding treatment services for both inpatient and outpatient care. Self-administered relaxation is ideally suited for problems in which anxiety is a major component and easily lends itself for use in "homework" assignments between therapy sessions. In general, self-administered relaxation can provide benefits as a treatment in itself or it can be used in conjunction with additional therapeutic techniques.

Case Study

The patient was a bright, 40-year-old married male with a lengthy history of chronic anxiety and related discomforts. When he was seen initially, he had been unemployed for a long period of time, had recently attempted suicide, and was generally quite anxious and depressed. Scores on the State-Trait Anxiety Inventory (9) indicated a State score of 74 and a Trait score of 64, both of which are indicative of a high level of anxiety. The outward manifestations of anxiety such as face flushed and perspiration on forehead were also observed during this time.

The treatment plan centered around reducing his anxiety and assisting him in achieving a more satisfactory over-all adjustment. Treatment began with a 1-hour session in which the procedures for self-administered relaxation training were explained. The patient was also provided with excerpts from *You Must Relax* (4) and cassette tapes on relaxation training (6). He was instructed to read the material provided and to go conscientiously through the exercises presented on the relaxation tapes. One week was allowed for familiarizing himself with the procedures involved. He was then instructed to carry out self-administered relaxation for a 4-week period by listening to the tapes at home and carrying out the exercises on his own. At the completion of this 4-week period, he reported that he felt more relaxed and less anxious. State-Trait anxiety was again measured at this time. The patient's State anxiety level decreased from 74 to 43, and his Trait anxiety level was reduced from 64 to 55. The patient also reported and appeared to be more relaxed. He further stated that he felt that he had mastered the technique of self-relaxation described on the tapes and was able to relax himself on his own. Aside from an occasional severe situational stress temporarily raising his anxiety level, 5 months after the completion of his 4 weeks of self-administered relaxation training, he reported the continued success in controlling excessive anxiety by self-administered relaxation exercises. His behavior remained the same at 10-, 15-, and 20-month follow-ups. By the tenth month follow-up the patient reported that he had obtained a job 4 months earlier that he was satisfied with and generally appeared to be maintaining an adequate over-all adjustment. This behavior was maintained at the fifteenth and twentieth month follow-ups.

Discussion

Self-administered relaxation training offers an effective treatment procedure for reducing chronic anxiety and related discomforts. During the 4-week treatment period, State anxiety decreased by 31 points and Trait anxiety by 9 points. At the end of the 4-week treatment period, at a time when the patient was more susceptible to counseling, the GED was successfully passed, he enrolled in a local junior college under the GI Bill, and obtained a part-time job. His total income from the GI Bill and part-time work provided a suitable income on which he could support himself and his family while, at the same time, learning a trade. His developed profiiciency in muscle relaxation enabled him to continue on and complete 15 months (as of last follow-up) of a two-year training program as well as obtain and maintain steady employment for a 14-month-plus period.

Perhaps the major value of self-administered relaxation training lies in its playing a supportive role in relation to other therapeutic techniques. The major value of this procedure is its ease, practicality, and efficiency. Self-administered relaxation can "set the stage" for the application of additional techniques which may not otherwise be applied. Relaxation tapes are readily available commercially, and for that matter, can also be prepared by either the patient or the therapist. Self-administered relaxation may be utilized in conjunction with medical treatment for lowering high blood pressure as well as in reducing preoperative tension in patients getting ready for surgery. Self-administered relaxation training can also be of benefit to psychiatric patients and "normal" individuals suffering from a variety of discomforts. In short, self-administered relaxation has

RELAX 157

therapeutic value in itself or when used in conjunction with additional behavioral techniques such as systematic desensitization, assertive training, and related methods. Self-administered relaxation is not offered as a panacea but rather as an efficient, practical procedure for expanding and extending existing treatment services.

REFERENCES

1. Allen, G. J. Treatment of test anxiety by group-administered and self-administered relaxation and study counseling. *Behavior Therapy*, 1973, 4, 349-360.
2. Dawley, H. H., L. M. Floyd, & C. A. Smith. Self-administered, minimal therapist contact, and automated behavior therapy: an annotated bibliography. *JSAS Catalog of Selected Documents in Psychology*, 1974, 4, No. 16.
3. Denholtz, M. The use of tape recordings between therapy sessions. *Journal of Behavior Therapy and Experimental Psychiatry*, 1970, 1, 139-143.
4. Jacobson, E. *You Must Relax*. New York: McGraw-Hill, 1962.
5. Kahn, M. & B. Baker. Desensitization with minimal therapist contact. *Journal of Abnormal Psychology*, 1968, 73, 198-200.
6. Lazarus, A. *Daily living: coping with tensions and anxieties*. Chicago: Instructional Dynamics, 1970.
7. Mahoney, M. J., & C. E. Thoresen. *Self-control: power to the person*. Belmont: Brooks/Cole, 1974.
8. Migler, B., & J. Wolpe. Automated self-desensitization: a case report. *Behavior Research and Therapy*, 1967, 5, 133-135.
9. Spielberger, C., R. Gorsuch, & R. Lushene. *State-Trait Anxiety Inventory*. Palo Alto, Calif.: Consulting Psychologists Press, 1970.
10. Thoresen, C. E., & M. J. Mahoney. *Behavioral Self-Control*. New York: Holt, Rinehart & Winston, 1974.
11. Watson, D. L., & R. G. Tharp. *Self-directed behavior: self-modification for personal adjustment*. Belmont: Brooks/Cole, 1972.
12. Wenrich, W. W., H. H. Dawley & D. General. *Self-directed systematic desensitization: behavior therapy for the client, student and therapist*. Kalamazoo: Behaviordelia, in press.

BIOFEEDBACK TRAINING FOR ANXIETY TENSION REDUCTION

ELMER E. GREEN, ALYCE M. GREEN, AND E. DALE WALTERS

Biofeedback is defined as the immediate ongoing presentation of information to a person concerning his own physiological processes. A patient looking at his own ongoing electrocardiographic (EKG) record is, by definition, getting biofeedback; if he tries to manipulate the heart through internal processes in some way while watching his record, using EKG feedback for guidance, he is trying biofeedback training.

Feedback for control of the striate muscles (voluntary nervous system) is the way in which every skill is learned—driving a car, for example—but it was not recognized until recently that the autonomic (involuntary) and central nervous systems could be self-regulated to a significant degree with the aid of biofeedback. In some way that is not yet fully understood, immediate knowledge of results develops awareness of normally undetected (normally unconscious) existential cues whose manipulation results in the changes desired. It should be noted that this process of control includes striate behavior. No one really knows how any volitional act is accomplished. All we know is that as babies we begin to practice controlling the striate system (probably because feedback is always available), but it is still unknown how we move our hands from one position to another. We visualize what we wish to do, give the "command" (whatever that is), and the act is carried out.

Autogenic feedback training for self-regulation of temperature (blood flow) has already been shown to be clinically effective in many patients in control of migraine headache (1, 2). Reynaud's disease, a deficiency of circulation in peripheral parts of the body, also has been reported in pilot work to yield to temperature training (3, 4). Tension headache yields to electromyographic (EMG) feedback training (5), and a host of cardiovascular studies

is showing promise for clinical control of a number of
cardiac disabilities and hypertension (6–8). Very recently
Sterman and Friar (9) have shown that epilepsy may be
brought under control through EEG feedback training for
elicitation in the sensory-motor brain region of a 12–14
Hertz (cycles/second) rhythm, and Poirier (10) has reported self-regulation of epilepsy through training of alpha
rhythm (8–13 Hz) in the occipital portion of the brain.

Although the foregoing reports of biofeedback research
and application involve the use of specific physiological
signals for the self-regulation of specific identifiable somatic
or psychosomatic disabilities, some biofeedback training is
especially useful in combatting generalized anxiety tension
reactions. Haugen, Dixon, and Dickel (11) showed that a
relaxation program aided on occasion by EMG feedback
was useful in training patients to handle their own tension
reactions, eventually "turning them off" without drugs. It
is interesting that the described psychiatric problems were
often solved in the process. Recently Paul Kurtz (12) began a biofeedback program involving, in part, anxiety reduction for the control of alcoholism and drug addiction.
More will be said about Kurtz's program, but first it may
be useful to provide a rationale to support the idea of
biofeedback training for anxiety tension reduction.

There is no certainty about the neural mechanisms involved in "voluntary controls" training, but there seems
little doubt that processes in the limbic-hypothalamic
axis are essential factors. Papez (13) laid the groundwork
for a neurological mechanism associated with emotion,
and additional work has elaborated his position (14). The
limbic system (the "visceral," or "emotional" brain) seems
to be the most significant subcortical responder to psychological stress in the central nervous system. It appears
from circumstantial evidence that chronic psychosomatic
problems are in some way the reflection of chronic im-
balances in the limbic-hypothalamic network, which in
turn affects the autonomic nervous system.

The chain of events involved in biofeedback for control
of autonomic processes might be hypothesized as follows:
Perception of somatic behavior (though biofeedback) →
cortical (cognitive) elaboration → limbic (emotional) response → hypothalamic response → autonomic response
→ somatic response → perception of somatic behavior, etc.

How volition enters into this scheme for self-regulation is not easy to say, but in any event each person becomes his own programmer, so to speak, when through biofeedback, self-regulation of a physiological process is established.

The question of volition, the essence of the mind-body problem, is not of course answered by these considerations. Whether volition is a metaforce that intersects the physiological matrix in some way, or whether a "king nucleus" of brain tissue operating in random fashion is the physiological origin of volition, cannot yet be determined. Regardless of its source, its existence is of great importance, because through the use of volition, self-determined changes can be initiated. Somewhere in the chain of processes volition becomes effective. The significance of this fact is just beginning to become apparent in clinical use of biofeedback training for recovery from psychosomatic disease without drugs. Nevertheless, the questions might be raised: How can biofeedback training be of any value in alcoholism or drug addiction? What is to be fed back? After all, if a person has migraine, biofeedback training involves learning to control the vascular system. If he suffers from tension headache, the preferred biofeedback method involves muscle tension feedback. Heart problems require feedback of heart behavior, hypertension requires feedback of blood pressure, and epilepsy requires feedback of brainwave pattern. What variable should be fed back in alcoholism, or drug addiction? These were the very questions, in fact, that I put to Paul Kurtz after presenting biofeedback seminars for a day at the unit for treatment of alcoholism and drug addiction in the St. Cloud Hospital, St. Cloud, Minnesota.

His response, somewhat paraphrased, was, "But you have overlooked what the problem really is in alcoholics. They think they cannot control anything for certain. They feel that they are robots of some kind. They feel that they can't guarantee their behavior because they are victims of impulses and compulsions completely beyond their capacity to handle.

"The first step is to demonstrate to them that this is not true. By the time an alcoholic learns to warm his hands 10°F at will, reduce his muscle tension levels to near zero, and increase his percentage of alpha rhythm, he will know, not just hope, or believe, that some processes are under his control. When that happens, he has essentially initiated a re-stabilization of maladjusted homeostatic processes (blood chemical changes will perhaps take place, associated with total relaxation and with focus of attention on self-aware-ness, as in transcendental meditation)" (15).

Kurtz's comments on the effects of "knowing" were im-pressive because I had shortly before received a letter say-ing similar things from a man who had been a volunteer subject in a 15-minute demonstration of autogenic training for control of hand temperature. This person sat with closed eyes before an audience, supposedly visualizing whole-body "heaviness" (relaxation) and warmth in his hands during the training session. Instead of warming, however, his hand temperature dropped 7°F in a few minutes. At the end of the demonstration, I asked him to describe to the audience his physical sensations and his mental and emotional reac-tions. He said that close to the beginning of the session his fingers began to tingle and he thought, "This must be warmth," and he added, "and I really made them tingle. One time I read a book on self-hypnosis and it said you could make your fingers tingle. I learned to do that."

Medical people present were aware of the fact that tin-gling in the fingers is generally associated with vasoconstric-tion and coolness, rather than with vasodilation and warmth. They realized that the subject had mistakenly cooled his hands rather than warmed them. My comment was that the demonstration was a real success, because it had illustrated the main point—that the body has a ten-dency to do what it is told if one knows how to correctly give instructions (through mental, auditory, or somatic visualization and feeling).

Two months after the demonstration, I got a letter from this man saying that his 15-minute exercise in self-regula-tion of hand temperature had made a significant change in his life. He confessed that until his demonstration he had really believed, deep down, that he did not have control of anything. But in the two months since the demonstration, he had succeeded in losing twelve pounds and was also able for the first time to answer his business corespondence in the first hour of each day. Neither of these things had been pos-sible until he realized (knew) that he had some power to make changes in himself.

With this illustration fresh in mind, it was quite clear

what Kurtz was driving at with respect to alcoholics. Therefore, when the opportunity came to discuss voluntary control techniques with respect to alcoholism, I called him to find out what had happened in his voluntary controls program.

His first problem was getting biofeedback machinery, temperature trainers, alpha-theta brainwave trainers, and a muscle tension trainer. A couple of months ago a preliminary study was begun with six hospitalized patients. Four were "chemically dependent," ranging in age from 16 to 20 years (one boy, three girls), and two were alcoholics (a man in his sixties and a woman who was 48 years old). The group practiced with the machines for four weeks, five days per week, one hour per day. In addition to biofeedback training, three of the young people and the older woman received training in a relaxing meditation. The reason for combining biofeedback and meditation in the preliminary study was that Kurtz wished to include, when it seemed appropriate, any voluntary controls method that he thought might work. In the design of a future research project, however, the variables would be separated.

Surprisingly, all six of the patients obtained a high degree of freedom from drugs or alcohol. In addition, all of them are still practicing "relaxation" exercises after two months. Feedback is not needed, incidentally, after the desired skill is fully learned. The most obvious personality change, found in every patient, was a newly developed freedom from petty tensions and minor irritations. They became "more manageable while in the hospital and at the same time retained independence." Not least, perhaps, all of them became more cheerful.

This close-to-total success may be in part a chance occurrence, but these findings are definitely provocative. Perhaps we should not be too surprised at these results, however, because the degree of relaxation that can be achieved from biofeedback training in temperature and muscle tension control is sizeable.

Muscle tension reduction is obviously correlated with relaxation, but the significance of an increase in hand temperature is not obvious. Raising the temperature of the hands is part of an exercise from autogenic training, a voluntary controls system begun by Johannes Schultz, a German physician, in about 1910. Schultz found that learning to control muscle tension and warmth in the body was associated with recovery from many psychosomatic diseases (16). More recently, Luthe (17) has edited a series of six volumes in which autogenic therapy is discussed from every angle.

To return to the hand-warming exercise: an increase of warmth in the hands is associated with an increase in blood flow. In laboratory-type research with over 100 subjects, we have observed a perfect correlation in every case between hand warmth and blood flow. Increased blood flow, in turn, results from vasodilation, and vasodilation in the hands is apparently dependent only on the decrease in neural outflow in the sympathetic section of the autonomic nervous system. In other words, in order to warm the hands by voluntary control, it is necessary to "turn off" autonomic (sympathetic) activation, that is, to relax autonomically. This, incidentally, seems to be the essential factor in hand temperature training for migraine control. When the sympathetic activation level is reduced, in addition to warming the hands, it apparently "wipes out" dysfunction in other sections of the vascular system. The blood flow problem in the head disappears when healthy homeostasis is restored.

Thus, through EMG and temperature feedback training, the peripheral nervous system is relaxed. Anxiety tension is reduced. When alpha-theta feedback is included in a training program, a state of "calmness" also ensues in the central nervous system. Whatever the neurological and hormonal details, the total effect tends toward emotional tranquility coupled with increased self-awareness and a sense of self-mastery.

To some it may sound too good to be true, and perhaps it is, but it does make sense, both neurologically and psychologically, and corresponds with other integrative findings from biofeedback research (18-20).

In conclusion, it seems that a general state of anxiety tension reduction coupled with increased self-awareness may be the preferred goal in biofeedback training for alcoholism and drug addiction. The sense of self-mastery that ensues from successful self-regulation is no doubt of considerable value. A general state of tension is most easily handled, we believe, through the use of biofeedback devices that reach all three sections of the nervous system—striate, autonomic, and central. Many of these ideas have yet to be tested, but in working with biofeedback subjects we often remind them that in psychosomatic disease it is not life that kills patients; it is, instead, their reaction to it. Aided by biofeedback, a person can learn to modify his emotional reaction so that continuous psychological stress will not perpetuate chronic somatic distortion. Perhaps psychosomatic health, rather than psychosomatic disease, can be self-chosen.

REFERENCES

1. Sargent, J., E. Green & D. Walters. 1972. The use of autogenic feedback training in a pilot study of migraine and tension headaches. Headache *12:* 120–124.
2. Sargent, J., D. Walters & E. Green. 1973. Psychosomatic self-regulation of migraine and tension headaches. *In* Seminars in Psychiatry. *5:* 415–428.
3. Sargent, J. 1973. Personal communication.
4. Gladman, A. 1973. Personal communication.
5. Budzynski, T., J. Stoyva & C. Adler. 1971. Application to tension headache. *In* Biofeedback and Self-Control. T. X. Barber *et al.,* Eds. Aldine-Atherton, Inc. Chicago, Ill.
6. Barber, T. X. *et al.,* Eds. 1971. Biofeedback and Self-Control. Aldine-Atherton, Inc. Chicago, Ill.
7. Kamiya, J. 1971. *In* Biofeedback and Self-Control. T. X. Barber *et al.,* Eds. Aldine-Atherton, Inc., Chicago, Ill.
8. Stoyva, J. 1971. *In* Biofeedback and Self-Control. T. X. Barber *et al.,* Eds. Aldine-Atherton, Inc. Chicago, Ill.
9. Sterman, M. B. & L. Friar. 1972. Suppression of seizures in an epileptic following sensorimotor EEG feedback training. Electroenceph. Clin. Neurophysiol. *33:* 89–95.
10. Poirier, F. 1972. Control of epilepsy through alpha training. Paper given at Annual Meeting of the Biofeedback Research Society, Boston, Mass., November, 1972.
11. Haugen, G. B., H. H. Dixon & H. A. Dickel. 1963. A Therapy for Anxiety Tension Reactions. The MacMillan Co. New York, N.Y.
12. Kurtz, P. 1972. Personal communication.
13. Papez, J. W. 1937. A proprosed mechanism of emotion. Arch. Neurol. Psychiat. *28:* 725–743.
14. Brady, J. V. 1958. The paleocortex and behavioral motivation. *In* Biological and Biochemical Bases of Behavior. H. F. Harlow & C. N. Woolsey, Eds. University of Wisconsin Press, Madison. Wisc.

15. Wallace, R. K. 1970. Physiological effects of transcendental meditation. Science *167*: 1751–1754.
16. Schultz, J. H. & W. Luthe. 1959. Autogenic Training: A Psychophysiologic Approach in Psychotherapy. Grune & Stratton, New York, N.Y.
17. Luthe, W., Ed. 1969. Autogenic Therapy, Vol. I–VI. Grune & Stratton. New York, N.Y.
18. Green, E., A. Green & D. Walters. Biofeedback for mind-body self-regulation: Healing and creativity. Proceedings of the Symposium on the Varieties of Healing Experience, De Anza College, Cupertino, Calif., October 30, 1971. The Academy of Parapsychology and Medicine, Los Altos, Calif.
19. Green, A., E. Green & D. Walter. 1973. Brainwave Training, Imagery, Creativity and Integrative Experiences. Unpublished report. The Menninger Foundation, Topeka, Kansas.
20. Kamiya, J. 1969. Operant control of the EEG alpha rhythm and some of its reported effects on consciousness. *In* Altered States of Consciousness. C. T. Tart, Ed. John Wiley & Sons, Inc. New York, N.Y.

MEDITATION AND THE PSYCHOTHERAPIST

THOMAS KEEFE

Only because of human thought and the delusion of being and non-being are our lives caught up in anxiety and dragged into suffering, conflict, hopelessness, and despair. Therefore, in the posture which lets go of our ideas we discover the absolute peace of life.[10]

Meditation has usually carried the connotation of contemplation and reflective thinking in the West. The term identifies different behavior in the context of Eastern mysticism or religious traditions. However, consideration and investigation of meditation behavior and technique need not be concomitant with the suspension of rational thought required by the belief systems associated with mysticism and religion. Like dialectical thought in the nineteenth century and like acupuncture more recently, meditation is a potentially useful technique that has begun a rapid diffusion into Western culture. [8, 18] The possibility that meditation, in its Eastern context, is potentially facilitative for the psychotherapist and conducive to interpersonal functioning in general is the impetus for this article.

The three-fold purposes of this article are to: 1) identify potential barriers to consideration and investigation of meditation as a behavior-changing technique, 2) define and describe meditation behavior, and 3) propose ways in which meditation might enhance both interpersonal functioning and therapist effectiveness.

Barriers to Investigation

The behavioral researcher or psychotherapist encounters certain natural barriers that could retard interest in investigation of meditation or limit its consideration as a potentially useful behavior modifying technique. Meditation arises from highly evolved introspective traditions that have employed subjective investigation and report. Objective scrutiny of meditation behavior, however, must rely upon electronic device or controlled study of its impact upon other more accessible behaviors. Subjects and investigators who would render meditation understandable and, eventually perhaps, useful in psychotherapy must be open to both subjective and objective modes of investigation. This does not mean that meditation behavior and its results are not reducible to explanation in terms of brain function. Nor does it suggest that the subjective experiences of the mediator, while lawful, can be fully encompassed in the explanations of a materially based science any more than can desire, subjective distress, purpose, hope, or consciousness.

Yogic Hinduism, the various forms of Buddhism including Zen, and some Christian sects employ meditation as a technique for spiritual or consciousness enhancement. Because it is rooted in traditions combining the religious and philosophical as well as the sociological and psychological, study of meditation or use of meditation in psychotherapy, in a sense, is to render the sacred secular. In this vein Fenwick,[4] discussing research related to the neurophysiology of meditation, states,

Some opportunity is now needed for professional workers such as doctors, social workers, and psychiatrists to learn the techniques of meditation, without the heavy overlay of Eastern philosophy, so that they can study its effects more precisely and assess its usefulness as a therapy technique.

Empirical investigation of meditation has begun with interesting results. A variety of psychological and physiological changes are reported in research cited secondarily by the Transcendental Meditation Society. Results include lowered metabolic rates, increased alpha wave pattern production, and higher galvanic skin response.[15] Goyeche et al[6] reported decreased respiration rates together with greater ease of maintenance when comparing Zen concentration with cotensive concentration. Van Nuys[17] found that deeper levels of meditation correspond with less intrusion into the attention of the meditator.

Boudreau[1] moved closer to areas of interest to the therapist when he used meditation techniques in successful treatment of claustrophobia and profuse perspiration after systematic desensitization produced only partial alleviation of the problems. Of additional interest to psychotherapists, meditation has been found to be productive of enhanced empathic ability[9] and to correlate with various measures of enhanced interpersonal functioning.[11] Given the extensive research[16] of Truax, Carkhuff, Mitchell, and others supporting the importance of therapist empathy, non-possessive warmth, genuineness, or self congruence, a technique useful in enhancement of these conditions in the therapist is of importance in the helping professions. Just how meditation is useful in enhancing empathy and other therapist behaviors will be discussed following a description of meditation behavior.

Meditation Behavior

While there are a variety of meditation schools arising from the several Eastern traditions, their pervading similarity is the minimization of thought in the verbal, linear, analytic sense.

Whether of Hindu, Buddhist, Zen, or other origin, meditation behavior usually entails concentration of attention and awareness on a single idea, object, or point inside or on the body. In addition to concentration, designed to bring the mind to "one-pointedness" and render to it a degree of self-control, postural requisites are levied upon the meditator usually with the objective of avoiding cramping and sleep. While there are a wide variety of positions, the familiar lotus position—seated cross-legged with back and neck erect, head balanced, and arms resting upon the knees or folded in the lap—is most commonly recognized as a meditation position.

These are variations in meditation object. It could be the breath, an internal point in the middle of the body, a point between the eyes, or a point beneath the spine. An external object (mandala) might be a candle, a picture or a design. Meditation upon an idea, symbol, verbal phrase, or puzzle (Koan) are other variations.

The goals of meditation also vary in accordance with the philosophical, religious, or social context. Meditation is practiced for the side effects of relaxation and calming, for the spiritual pursuit of enlightenment, for the dissolution of the subject-object mode of perception, for enhanced interpersonal functioning and empathy, or for greater insight into one's feelings and self. Sometimes, especially in Soto Zen, meditation is practiced for no explicit goal at all and, indeed, entails the relinquishment of goals and their pursuit.

Meditation is not a trance. Awareness is sharpened. Meditation is universally a *tuning in* to higher or more refined perception and awareness, not a *tuning out* or a severance of sensory input. The interference with concentration upon the meditation object by sensory input, verbal or visual thoughts, feelings, and one's social role expectations are at first frequent. When the meditator's awareness and attention are distracted to something sensed, thought, or felt, it is brought back to focus on the meditation object. Distracting thoughts or perceptions are allowed to pass in and out of awareness without being pursued or built upon by the verbal, analytic mind. Increasingly one's ability to maintain concentration is developed. Sensory input is still received, even enhanced (as, for instance, in sharper hearing due to lower thresholds), but the meditator does not become more than momentarily distracted, if at all. In this way, he or she slowly learns a degree of awareness without diverting attention from continued focus on the meditation object.

The meditation task is carried on for twenty to thirty minutes once or twice a day at first and then is usually extended. The beginner typically finds concentration difficult and learns that the undisciplined mind behaves much like a "drunken monkey" [2] in the sense of easy distractability, continuous verbal thought production, and lack of ability to rest empty of past and future preoccupation while firmly focused on a single point of attention in *present time*.

As the meditator proceeds, he or she learns that relaxing the eye muscles and muscles of the tongue and throat eases the production of visual and verbal thought. The meditator slowly acquires enhanced control over attention and concentration. He or she develops a conscious ability to enter a meditative state at will and empty the mind of preoccupation or distracting thoughts. Relaxation is more easily accessible, somatic events are more vividly experienced or even controlled, and complex cognitive processes can be held in abeyance to facilitate perception or concentration behaviors. In short, there are a number of behaviors learned in meditation that may be functionally transferred to interpersonal or therapeutic behavior, as shall be illustrated.

Enhancement of Therapist Effectiveness

Three main behavioral products of meditation facilitative to therapeutic behavior and interpersonal functioning are suggested: 1) enhanced awareness of one's own feelings; 2) increased ability to hold complex cognitive processes in abeyance to enhance perception; and 3) enhanced capacity to maintain a focus of attention and awareness upon present events—in other words, to be in the here-and-now.

As described, meditation requires a reduction in sensory and information input. The resultant increase in awareness of somatic conditions and ability to turn attention and awareness to these conditions coincides with Rich's *inner directed attention,* so vital as a meaningful guide to one's responses to the feeling states and presentations of others.[12] The capacity to know how one reacts to another person and to feed the information back to that person is a prerequisite to a therapist facilitating accurate empathy.

Contemporary phenomenological psychologies and psychotherapies have a parallel in the meditative traditions of the East. Abraham Maslow, in his study of self actualizing persons, postulated "Being Cognition," which was conceived of as a twofold process. The first stage is a desireless awareness, a non-judgmental, passive, and receptive perceptual behavior wherein the perceiver momentarily, at least, is less affected than usual by his or her own desires, hopes, or fears. The perceiver thus sees the world more as it *is* than as he or she would *have* it be. The second stage of the perceptual process is a discriminating guide to action. Jourard [7] compares what he calls *transcendant perception,* not unlike the first stage of "Being Cognition," with the typical Western mode of perceiving, in saying:

> We usually observe the world under the impetus and direction of our needs, values, feelings and purposes of the moment. Such need-steered perception certainly serves a vital role in our survival and adaptation; but it also tends to blind us to all features of the world that are not immediately relevant to our present hungers, desires and values. "Desireless," or "undriven" cognition—when we simply open our eyes, ears, noses, taste buds, kinesthetic and organic receptors and let stimuli play upon them and impress them —seems to be the condition for the enriched mode of perception. [7]

"Being cognition" and transcendant perception are remarkably like the *bare attention* behavior described by Thera:

> It cleans the object of investigation from the impurities of prejudice and passion; it frees it from alien admixtures and from points of view not pertaining to it; it holds it before the Eye of Wisdom, by slowing down the transition from the receptive to the active phase of the perceptual or cognitive process, thus giving a vastly improved chance for close and dispassionate investigation. [14]

The enhanced ability, acquired in meditation, to temporarily and voluntarily suspend verbal and visual thought is a behavior facilitative to enhanced interpersonal perception. Other persons may be perceived momentarily as they *are* and allowed, as it were, to speak for themselves, prior to diagnostic categorization or scrutiny through a screen of preconceptions.

Various schools of psychotherapy arising from an existential base, as well as specific approaches to conjoint therapy, emphasize a capacity to be in the moment with the patient or client,[3] and deemphasize the use of historical or out-of-session material. Most psychotherapies, regardless of temporal emphasis, stress moment-to-moment attention to the ongoing communication process, feeling responses, and content of the therapeutic interaction. Whether used as an aid in reality testing or interpretation, whether used to reflect upon one's own responses or to describe observed behavior, a capacity to relate to the here-and-now realities of the several levels of interaction and behavior in therapy session or other interpersonal interaction is essential to the therapist and useful to the fully functioning person. The enhanced ability to attune to the moment, gained in meditation, becomes invaluable when applied in therapeutic or other interpersonal encounters.

In summary, seeing another as he or she is, consciously sensing one's feeling responses to that person and attending, when appropriate, closely to the moment-to-moment events and levels of the interaction can enhance therapeutic effectiveness of practitioners. In addition to enhancing these behaviors, evidence supports the positive impact of meditation upon empathy.

Summary and Conclusion

Though widely divergent, the psychophilosophical traditions of East and West can be sources of continued cross fertilization of behavior and artifact, rendering both cultures the richer. The divergent approaches to knowledge are not necessarily exclusive but may indeed be highly complementary.[13] In this light, potential barriers to the investigation and consideration of meditation on the part of researchers and psychotherapists were discussed as an introduction to the description of meditation behavor and a discussion of the potential usefulness of meditation to the psychotherapist and in general interpersonal functioning.

Behaviors transferred from meditation and potentially facilitative to therapist effectiveness and interpersonal functioning include enhanced awareness of one's own feelings, increased ability to hold complex cognitive processes in abeyance, enhanced perception, and increased present-centeredness.

Meditation is increasingly the subject of empirical study, and its derivative behaviors are compatible with and facilitative of therapist behavior in traditional and developing schools of psychotherapy. Meditation is becoming a less esoteric, more legitimate, subject of both subjective and empirical investigation. Meditation may be found to be a potent tool for the psychotherapist in the facilitation of his or her own effectiveness and in the enhancement of interpersonal functioning in general.

REFERENCES

1. Boudreau, L. 1972. Transcendental meditation and yoga reciprocal inhibitors. J. Behav. Ther. Exper. Psychiat. 3:97–98.
2. Dass, B. 1971. From bindu to otas. In Be Here Now. Crown Publishing, New York.
3. Ehrenkranz, S. 1967. A study of joint interviewing in the treatment of marital problems. Soc. Casewk. 48:498–501; 48:570–574.
4. Fenwick, P. 1973. The neurophysiology of meditation. Intellectual Dig. (Nov.).
5. Gobel, F. 1970. The Third Force. Pocket Books, New York. (p. 27)
6. Goyeche, J., Chliarci, T. and Shemizer, H. 1972. Two concentration methods: a preliminary comparison. Psychologia 15:110–111.
7. Jourard, S. 1966. Psychology of transcendent perception. In Explorations in Human Potential, H. Otto, ed. Charles C. Thomas, Springfield, Ill. (p. 354)
8. Jung, C. 1947. On the psychology of eastern meditation. In Art and Thought. Luyac, London.
9. Keefe, T. 1973. Empathy: Impact of Social Work Education and Enhancement Techniques. University of Utah dissertation, Salt Lake City.
10. Kosho, U. 1973. Approach to Zen. Japan Publications, San Francisco. (p. 112).
11. Lesh, T. 1971. Zen meditation and the development of

Barber *et al*, eds. Aldene-Atherton, Chicago.
 observational process in casework. *In* Exemplars of Social Research, P. Fetlin *et al*, eds. Peacock Publishers, Itasca, Ill.
13. Ten Houten, W. and Kaplan, C. 1973. Science and Its Mirror Image, A Theory of Inquiry. Harper & Row, New York.
14. Thera, N. 1962. The Heart of Buddhist Meditation. Samuel Weiser, Inc., New York.
15. Transcendental Meditation. 1973. International Meditation Society, Los Angeles.
16. Truax, C. and Mitchell, K. 1971. Research on certain therapist interpersonal skills in relation to process and outcome. *In* Handbook of Psycho-Therapy and Behavior Change, A. Bergin and S. Garfield, eds. John Wiley, New York.
17. Van Nuys, D. 1971. A novel technique for studying attention during meditation. J. Transpersonal Psychol. 3:125–133.
18. Watts, A. 1953. Asian psychology and modern psychology. Amer. J. Psychoanal. 1:13.

From *PROGRESSIVE RELAXATION*

EDMUND JACOBSON

Who Can Be Relaxed?

(THE INFLUENCE OF AGE, PERSONAL TYPE, OCCUPATION, VARIOUS DISEASE CONDITIONS AND OTHER FACTORS)

In practice I found that relaxation could be taught to willing patients much the same as golfing, skating, pianoforte, or driving a motor car are accessible to the average person. Degrees of skill acquired will, of course, differ greatly according to the character and degree of cooperation of the patient, the distractions produced by physical or emotional conditions or by circumstances, and the efficacy of the teaching. Much depends upon the amount of time allotted for practice, and the physician needs to devote considerable energy and patience to the difficult, distracted patient.

I found that singers, dancers and athletes may learn very rapidly owing to a certain prior familiarity with muscular tension and relaxation. As would be expected, healthy individuals (the subjects were university students and doctors) learn more quickly than do patients with distress. During neurosis, distraction on the part of the patient tends to prolong the learning period. Children may require special methods of training. The youngest in my experience was an intelligent child of eight and one-half years, who learned very readily. I succeeded, not perfectly but very markedly, in relaxing a girl of thirteen years who was of subnormal intelligence (I.Q. 53–57, three tests, Terman modification of Binet-Simon scale), indicating that a high intelligence quotient is not required for the present method. My oldest patient was sixty-eight; she made noteworthy progress, but the results were, of course, far from perfect. Old age, therefore, is not an insuperable barrier.

It has been said that willingness is the cardinal requirement for the method of relaxation; yet this statement has to be modified. For as a rule, even the healthy adult would rather be up and doing than lying down to relax; in this he is like the child who does not wish to go to bed at night. Unwillingness to give up activities is increased during fretfulness and distress. Thus in disease, where relaxation is most needed, the conditions for inducing it become increasingly difficult. This is particularly true, for instance in toxic goiter, where the individual feels the drive to be doing yet shows evident need for relaxation. It therefore becomes the physician's task to overcome this unwillingness by argument, persuasion and every other means in his power; just as it is the business of the surgeon to overcome the opposition of his patients to needed operations. Fortunately, as the individual progressively relaxes, unwillingness gives way to the desire for rest and for the resulting comfort.

I have investigated whether methods of relaxation can be applied to certain forms of insanity, notably the manic-depressive variety. Here willingness is at times notably absent, and therefore the physician can only hope for rather than expect success. He must seek to induce relaxation by argument, persuasion, example and proper instructions to attendants. He must keep in mind that the disease is characterized by spontaneous recessions and therefore use great caution in attributing observed improvements to his methods. With these considerations in mind, our results, although unsuccessful in some cases, nevertheless suggest that the method can in principle be applied, and that the effort is justified.

The method to produce extreme relaxation is not in principle limited to chronic conditions where we wish to inculcate habits of rest. Often in medical practice a brief period of intensive rest is required for acute conditions of distress or exhaustion, and it may be desired to apply physiologic methods in place of bromides, morphine or other drug sedatives. The physician here encourages the patient to relax extremely, shows him briefly in a period or two how to do this and performs it himself for a few minutes by way of illustration for imitation. Treatment of the patient in acute distress (provided that pain is not too severe at the moment) is therefore open by this route, and the aim will be transitory alleviation of symptoms with consequent favoring of recovery, when possible.

The Christian Scientist, the theosophist, and in general the cultist are difficult subjects. These are the suggestible and dependent types, giving the physician an added task to make them rely upon themselves. They have many bizarre ideas which interfere with their learning to relax, and much time may be lost with them in argument. Patients inclined to credulity and excessive faith in the physician also generally fail to observe for themselves and take longer to learn to relax than do average indivduals. One cultist reported that she had hypnotized herself daily since childhood in order to go to sleep. This proved to be a difficulty when treatment by relaxation was begun, for she tended toward a hypnoidal condition. The attempt to relax her was therefore abandoned.

Since suggestibility is to a certain extent an impediment in being taught to relax, the hysterical individual sometimes offers marked difficulties. The physician must give directions precisely and make sure that no hypnoidal condition and no increased suggestibility results. Following these precautions, the hysterical subject, I believe, can generally be relaxed.

To What Disorders Does Relaxation Apply?

A consideration of the widespread application of rest to disease conditions leads us to anticipate widespread opportunity for the present method of intensive rest. In some disorders relaxation may appear as the principal or only method of treatment, while in others it may be adjuvant to other measures of surgery or medicine or hygiene. The physician will recall that the applications of methods of diet to the practice of medicine are manifold, requiring a large volume to describe them. Writers who recognize the importance of diet do not thereby offer it as a panacea, and there is likewise no such intent or purpose in presenting the present method of intensive rest.

An interesting experience is to observe the signs of excitement or distress diminish as the patient relaxes. It is difficult and not quite satisfactory, at the present stage of work, to present results statistically. If we consider the influence of intensive relaxation on the entire course of the malady, we lack an accurate quantitative measure of the effects. An added difficulty is that the maladies of individuals so far treated by the present method vary greatly and are not readily classed together for purposes of statistical calculations. Furthermore, it is difficult for one investigator alone to collect a large series of cases of one particular malady because of the generally long course of the condition and its treatment. Again, how shall we classify the results of treatment of nervousness, when favorable, but existing as a complication of incurable organic disease? Where the malady can be classed under two headings, which heading should be used?

Despite these limitations, the following tables may have some significance. Therapeutic agents other than relaxation were practically or entirely excluded in a number of cases selected for treatment and the results are presented in Table I. We present separately (Table II) the figures for certain other cases where some other form of treatment was used in addition to relaxation; for example, special diet in mucous colitis, iron or spleen-marrow where anemia accompanied nervous hypertension, or surgery for the removal of suspected focal infections. But such measures were generally directed toward the correction of complications and not toward the functional disorder under study;

except in a few cases, where some form of psychological treatment supplemented the relaxation. As will be seen, the results have warranted the expenditure of time and patience, and encourage the hope that others will be induced to apply the same methods. "Objective" results in Graves' disease include records of pulse, temperature, basal metabolism. In some instances the patients failed to remain under treatment for an extended period, but they are included in the tables when the duration has been long enough to seem significant even if the work was incomplete.

TABLE I

Disease	No. of Cases	Quit	Objective Result (Improvement)					Patient's Report (Improvement)			
			None	Slight	Marked	Very Marked	Doubtful	None	Slight	Marked	Very Marked
Nervous hypertension	31	6	0	6	14	11	0	0	2	11	18
Acute insomnia with nervousness	6	0	0	1	1	3	1	0	0	3	3
Anxiety neurosis	2	0	0	0	0	2	0	0	0	0	2
Cardiac neurosis	1	0	0	0	0	1	0	0	0	0	1
Chronic insomnia	12	7	0	5	2	3	2	0	2	3	7
Compulsion neurosis	1	0	0	0	0	1	0	0	0	0	1
Convulsive tic	3	1	0	0	1	2	0	0	0	1	2
Cyclothymic exaltation	2	1	0	0	1	0	1	0	0	0	2
Cyclothymic depression	7	2	0	0	2	5	0	1	0	1	5
Esophageal spasm	3	0	0	0	0	3	0	0	0	0	3
Graves' disease	3	0	0	1	2	0	0	0	1	1	1
Hypochondria	2	0	0	0	0	2	0	0	0	0	2
Mucous colitis	2	1	0	0	0	2	0	0	0	1	1
Spastic paresis	1	0	0	0	0	1	0	0	0	0	1
Stuttering, stammering	3	3	0	0	3	0	0	0	0	3	0
Unclassified psychosis	1	0	0	0	1	0	0	0	0	1	0
Cardiac asthma	1	0	0	0	1	0	0	0	0	1	0

Figures indicate results at end of treatment in cases where relaxation was the sole therapeutic measure. As a rule, each patient appears but once in the table, being placed under one heading, e.g., under "Mucous colitis" or "Nervous hypertension," even if his disease symptoms might properly be included under both headings. A considerable number of patients with symptoms classed "Nervous hypertension" might equally well be represented under "Hypochondria" or "Insomnia" but it is believed that singleness of representation of each patient in the table will give a fairer idea of results.

It has seemed best to avoid the use of the term "cure," partly in order to avoid the difficulty of distinguishing between this and "very marked improvement" and partly in order to err on the side of claiming too little rather than too much. In many instances, however, where the patient has persisted at re-education, the consequences have seemed quite thorough and have persisted for years.

Treatment limited approximately to relaxation alone was applied from 1929 to 1938 in 105 adidtional patients, as shown in Table III. The patients accepted this limitation in

TABLE II

Disease	No. of Cases	Quit	Objective Result (Improvement)					Patient's Report (Improvement)			
			None	Slight	Marked	Very Marked	Doubtful	None	Slight	Marked	Very Marked
Nervous hypertension	8	1	0	1	4	3	0	0	0	4	4
Anxiety neurosis	1	0	0	0	0	1	0	0	0	0	1
Chronic insomnia	1	1	0	0	0	0	1	1	0	0	0
Cyclothymic exaltation	1	0	1	0	0	0	0	0	0	1	0
Cyclothymic depression	2	1	0	0	1	0	1	0	0	1	1
Graves' disease	3	1	0	0	1	2	0	0	0	1	2
Mucous colitis	6	2	0	0	2	4	0	0	0	0	6
Unclassified colitis	1	0	0	0	0	1	0	0	0	0	1
Unclassified psychosis	1	0	0	1	0	0	0	0	0	1	0
Cardiac asthma	1	0	0	1	0	0	0	0	1	0	0
Bronchial asthma	1	0	0	0	0	1	0	0	0	0	1

Figures indicate results of treatment in cases where relaxation was the sole measure used for treatment of nervousness but where other measures, such as diet in colitis, or iron in anemia, or the surgical removal of infectious foci, were employed for the treatment of concomitant disease conditions.

order to learn what results might be due to relaxation and in order to eliminate sedatives or other medicines, if taken previously. These medicines were eliminated as soon as possible, even if they seemed indicated. In several instances, minor operations were postponed until toward or after the close of treatment. In colitis, as previously stated, laxatives, belladonna or other agents for chronic pain, as well as restrictions on diet, were gradually abolished.

Psychotherapeutic measures, including assurance to the patient of his ultimate recovery, were likewise, so far as possible, omitted. Deviations from this rule occurred in

TABLE III

Disorder	No. of Cases	Treatment Incomplete	Physician's Report (Improvement)					Patient's Report (Improvement)				
			None	Slight	Marked	Very Marked	Doubtful	None	Slight	Marked	Very Marked	Doubtful
Nervous hypertension	82	35	0	7	33	38	4	1	4	27	49	1
Fatigue states	17	4	0	0	5	11	1	0	0	3	14	0
Insomnia	34	18	0	6	12	15	1	0	4	13	17	0
Anxiety states	5	2	0	2	0	3	0	0	2	0	3	0
Nervous depression	7	2	0	2	1	4	0	0	2	1	4	0
Hypochondria	4	0	0	0	0	4	0	0	0	0	4	0
Phobias	5	0	0	0	1	4	0	0	0	1	4	0
Chronic colitis	25	11	0	2	6	16	1	0	2	5	18	0
Esophagus spasm	5	1	0	1	0	4	0	0	1	0	4	0
Sigmoiditis	1	0	0	0	0	1	0	0	0	1	0	0
Arterial hypertension	13	7	2	2	2	5	2	2	1	3	5	2
Nephritic hypertension	1	0	0	1	0	0	0	0	0	0	1	0
Tic	1	0	0	0	0	1	0	0	0	0	1	0
Facial spasm	1	1	1	0	0	0	0	1	0	0	0	0
Tension headaches	4	1	0	0	1	3	0	0	0	1	3	0
Ocular headaches	1	0	0	0	0	1	0	0	0	0	1	0
Facial neuralgia	1	1	1	0	0	0	0	1	0	0	0	0
Functional tachycardia	1	0	0	0	1	0	0	0	0	0	1	0
Coronary disease	1	0	0	0	1	0	0	0	0	1	0	0
Tremor	1	0	0	0	0	1	0	0	0	0	1	0
Dsymenorrhea	1	0	0	0	0	1	0	0	0	0	1	0
Cyclothymic depression	14	3	2	0	2	9	1	2	2	0	8	2
Cyclothymic exaltation	1	1	0	0	1	0	0	0	0	0	1	0
Mild alcoholism	1	1	0	0	0	1	0	0	0	0	1	0
Neurosis of bladder	1	1	0	0	1	0	0	0	0	0	1	0
Parkinson's disease	1	0	0	0	0	0	1	1	0	0	0	0
Stammering, stuttering	2	1	0	0	1	1	0	0	0	1	1	0

Figures for 105 additional patients (1929-37) treated by methods of relaxation, omitting other measures (see text).

cyclothymic depression, particularly when discouragement was so severe as to threaten suicide. In that event, any measure of psychotherapy or medicine was added, provided that it seemed to avert the danger, after which methods were again restricted to relaxation alone.

To complete the data for this table, 66 questionnaires were sent out in November, 1937, to which 38 replies were received. In the remaining 28 instances, data are based upon the condition of the patient as ascertained previously. In some instances the results refer to the condition at the termination of treatment; but in most they include also a subsequent period up to 6 years, provided that other treatment did not follow.

The present tables are based upon interpretations of complex data secured by various objective clinical and laboratory measures, but also upon the patient's observations. It is difficult, if not sometimes impossible, to estimate therapeutic results accurately. Since the results include the patients whose treatment was not complete, they are in this respect understated.

Indications for Treatment by Relaxation

The purpose of relaxation is to do away with certain activities that place an undue tax upon the organism. Since relaxation is the intensive form of rest, we may assume that it will be indicated as a rule where rest is indicated, a topic which was discussed in the early chapters. It is well for the physician to bear in mind that patients who are obviously restless and emotional are not the only ones who are in need of intensive rest. He may equally well investigate whether his cases of peptic ulcer, organic heart disease or diverse other conditions might not show subsidence of symptoms if in addition to other treatment their reflexes were to be quieted by relaxation. Pending many such investigations by others, we cannot here make final statements of indications for the present method. However, a tentative program may be suggested:

1. *Acute neuromuscular hypertension* (commonly called "nervousness" or "emotional disturbance").—This may occur during the course of a large variety of diseases and may be treated with sedative drugs, physiologic relaxation, or both.

2. *Chronic neuromuscular hypertension.*—This includes what is commonly called "neurasthenia," but appears also in all the "functional neuroses," such as phobias, tics, hab-

it spasm, insomnia, stammering and stuttering, emotional unbalance, and heightened reflexes without organic derangement. The psychic phases of neuromuscular hypertension are highly variable: they include worry, anxiety, hypochondria, inability to concentrate because of apparent restlessness, compulsions and the many and diverse symptoms sometimes termed psychasthenia. In certain conditions, the aim of treatment will be thoroughgoing: to remove by relaxation the groundwork of the neuromuscular disposition to neurosis; to do away with those static and other continual tensions which close clinical observation of the neurotic indivdual always discloses. In other conditions, the aim will be less ambitious, yet still remain of consequence: palliative, in the sense of removing a set of symptoms, where the underlying malady cannot be successfully reached.

3. *States of fatigue and exhaustion,* alone or in complication with disease. Prophylaxis by means of relaxation is also to be thought of here.

4. *States of debility.*—This would include convalescence from infectious and exhaustive diseases of various types. The present method appears appropriate in cases of retarded recovery where an element of rest might aid.

5. *Sundry preoperative and postoperative conditions.*— Writers on surgery are beginning to emphasize the importance of rest in preparation for the nervous strain of operation and the subsequent distress. The present method, in my experience, has appeared to reduce the patient's excitability and has seemed therefore to contribute to postoperative comfort. In several instances also, the effects of treating the "chronic complainer" subsequent to operation have seemed helpful.

6. *Toxic goiter.*—Plummer's extensive experience has led him to regard early operation as the most important and indispensable of treatments for the protection of the heart. Even the most successful operative statistics, however, do not claim 100 per cent of cures. In this disease there is room for a method of rest in conjunction with operation as well as where operation is not performed.

7. *Disturbances of sleep.*—These topics will be discussed in a later work. Treatment is commonly effective.

8. *Alimentary spasm,* including mucous colitis, colonic spasm, cardiospasm, and other esophagospasms.

9. *Peptic ulcer,* ascribed to nervous tendencies.

10. *Chronic pulmonary tuberculosis.*—Increasing popularity of rest in the treatment of this disease suggests that intensive relaxation may prove of service. The tendency might be to favor the healing of diseased tissue, in effect like pneumothorax. No reference is here intended to any process of immunity.

11. *Organic and functional heart disorders,* requiring rest.

12. *Vascular hypertension.*—This matter has been under investigation since 1921. In essential hypertension there is increased irritability in arterial and arteriolar musculature and eventual hypertrophy. Both systolic and diastolic pressure tend to fall as residual tension in skeletal muscles nears zero, as measured by action-potentials. Treatment seems promising even in difficult cases. One patient, for example, with diastolic pressure above 130 at least 6 years previously, now shows marked reduction with normal levels at times. High systolic pressures may yield more readily to prolonged treatment.

Since the importance of prevention in present-day medicine is generally recognized, it is evident that in disorders where the efficacy of relaxation has been established, the method of relaxation should be employed for prophylaxis as well as for treatment.

AUTOGENIC TRAINING

HANNES LINDEMANN

The originator of Autogenic Training was Dr. J. H. Schultz, who died in 1970 at age eighty-six, after a long and fruitful life. Schultz frequently observed that his father, a professor of theology at Göttingen, had been interested in saving souls, but that he was devoted to healing them.

In his youth Schultz had to suffer a great deal from his peers because of his fragility, a fate he shared with Sigmund Freud and many others, all of whom have shown us how, with the help of exemplary self-discipline, one can enjoy a long life despite a weak constitution.

After studying in Lausanne, Göttingen, and Breslau, Schultz worked for a while before World War I at the Paul Ehrlich Institute in Frankfurt. During a demonstration in psychotherapy—in connection with an experiment in hypnosis—Schultz placed a coin on the back of a young man's hand and told him that the coin was red hot and would burn his skin, though without hurting him. When the coin was removed, there was no trace of a burn. But two weeks later the man returned and reported that every morning he noticed a painless blister on the back of his hand which always disappeared in the course of the day. Schultz now remembered that he had failed to cancel the suggestion given to the man during the hypnosis. He canceled the suggestion immediately and the man's blisters ceased to appear.

After practicing as a dermatologist, Schultz became a neurologist. During World War I, he wrote his first major book, *Psychic Treatment of Diseases,* on the basis of which he was later named a full professor at the University of Jena. He then became chief physician in a well-known sanitarium near Dresden, and in 1924 he settled in Berlin as a psychiatrist. More than four hundred articles and many books testify to his great energy, and he made many valuable contributions to psychotherapy. Undoubtedly, however, his most important contribution was the development of Autogenic Training, which is forever linked to his name.

The Origins of Autogenic Training

As early as 1910 in Breslau, Schultz worked with hypnosis. It was during this period that his interest was aroused in a field known today as psychosomatic medicine. In an article he published in 1920, "The Stratification Levels in the Hypnotized Psyche," his basic concepts of AT are evident. Schultz said that people under hypnosis regularly experience two conditions: "A peculiar heaviness, especially in their limbs, and a peculiar warmth."

The core of hypnosis is a "central shift" that can be activated psychically or physically. Even then it was recognized that hypnosis really was the art of inducing the patient to make a self-hypnotic shift. It was important to make sure that the patient did not go totally to sleep.

In hypnosis, as in the practice of AT, the feelings of heaviness and warmth occur in connection with this shift. Schultz spoke of an "organismic psychosomatic shift," which, he said, also occurs if a person takes a "long relaxing bath" (Kraepelin).

Schultz then wanted the patients themselves to make the shift. He knew this was possible, for the researches of the neurologist Oskar Vogt had proven that people could "place themselves in a hypnotized condition by means of a complete shift." Therefore, Schultz recognized, patients had to relax and then induce in themselves the feelings of heaviness and warmth.

In the following years, with the help of some of his students and disciples, Schultz developed Autogenic Training to such a level that by 1932 he was ready to publish his great monograph, "Autogenic Training, Concentrative Self-Relaxation," the first edition of which was soon followed by further editions as well as translations.

In his preface to the seventh edition (1951), Schultz observed that because it had become a fad, many unqualified persons utilized Autogenic Training to relax themselves or others. He cited this as proof that relaxation exercises were already much in demand, and today they are even more important. Some people regard relaxation exercises as a fad without being aware of the intense longing and instinctive search for a means of combatting the stress of everyday life. Actually, even a fad will succeed only if it is accepted and if it fills a need. And AT *is* accepted: it has made friends all over the world, friends who would no longer want to be without it.

How to Learn Autogenic Training Most Easily

First of all, you must truly believe that you can learn AT. Every doubt about yourself and the method, or your teacher, makes the venture more difficult. A neutral attitude is good, a positive attitude is better.

It is also advantageous if there is an important reason for learning AT. Experience has shown that people who want merely to familiarize themselves with AT progress less well than those who wish to use it in pursuing specific aims. The best guarantee for learning the method quickly is a compelling motivation that can override any inner doubt and brush aside any uncertainty.

A "weak" personality will learn AT more easily than a "strong" one, because the latter's individual consciousness is strong and the ability to identify is weak. An absence of strong logical thinking helps one to learn Autogenic Training, as does firm confidence in its effect. The person who suffers and can accept events with equanimity will generally make better progress than the restless, nervous, active, and suspicious person.

Faith can help a great deal. Even though faith is not everyone's "thing," students of AT should try consciously to have the courage to believe, simply because "to give a person faith means to multiply his strength," as Gustave LeBon said in his *Psychology of the Masses*. The effectiveness of placebos demonstrates the strength of the psychology of faith in the power of a method or a drug.

"Placebo" derives from the Latin of "I will please." A placebo, a pseudodrug, has no active ingredients and is given to a patient instead of an active drug. The preparation may look like the real drug, but it usually contains only an ineffective and harmless substance like sugar. When neither the doctor nor the participants in the experiment know whether a placebo or a genuine drug is being administered, the experiment is termed "double-blind."

In the course of several double-blind experiments it was demonstrated that in 30 to 60 percent of the cases there were autosuggestive placebo effects. Most frequent was a positive effect in treatment of headaches.

One strongly inhibiting element in learning AT is the will: if the student makes excessive efforts, he thus precludes any success. We call this the "principle of paradoxical intentions." The conscious effort of the will stimulates and reinforces opposite impulses. An intense effort combined with gnawing doubts inhibit success. Dr. Schultz believed that the student should yield to his inclination to passivity and permit himself to slip into the AT state. The person who can relax and surrender himself to the moment is likely to master AT without much trouble.

When to Exercise

Schultz repeatedly pointed out that "only a systematic and precise procedure could bring the full effect and benefit of this method." In other words, the beginner should follow the instructions as closely as possible. A certain freedom of action may sometimes be justified, but for the majority of those who learn AT it is better to be quite systematic from the beginning.

Everyone will discover for himself the best time for exercise. Generally, the last exercise is best done before going to sleep. As we shall see, that has many advantages. To exercise every evening is absolutely necessary.

To begin the day with AT has also become a source of psychic well-being for many people. Anyone who thinks he can't afford these five minutes cheats himself; it is merely an excuse, or perhaps a sign of already excessive tension. Particularly in the morning a person can prove that he is not driven by his false ideas. To engage in AT in the morning will help you attain and maintain your perspective.

Several people have reported that they go back to sleep during their morning exercise. They were told to repeat the following formula during their exercise:

I stay free and fresh while training.

This formula should also be used when you are doing your training in the office or anywhere you do not wish to fall asleep.

The afternoon session is really only for those who are already somewhat more advanced. Done properly, it takes the place of a coffee break: after finishing the exercise, you will feel refreshed. The exercise can also help overcome the drowsiness that follows a meal.

The person who does not have a private office can still do his AT for a few minutes by isolating himself mentally from his colleagues.

The more regularly the exercises are undetaken. the more easily will the desired effects be produced.

Ten Minutes Daily

Initially, a person should allocate about one minute for the first exercise. Once he is more advanced, he should use about five minutes per exercise. If he adds a verbal formula incorporating certain resolutions, one exercise may take as much as ten minutes, but these ten minutes are an investment in health.

Generally, the student should practice three times a day. Once he is satisfied with his first successes, he will automatically move on to a "maintenance dosage"—the minimum being to exercise twice a day.

If it can be arranged, the exercising should take place in a slightly darkened and not overly warm room. The windows should be closed in order to eliminate disturbing noises.

It is not easy to train on a full stomach. The consumption of coffee will also generally make it difficult to concentrate—and the ability to concentrate is essential.

Sometimes the student can help himself and make the training easier by imagining that he has just returned from a long walk and now feels pleasantly tired.

There are as many reasons as there are individuals for the inability to collect one's thoughts. Some students state that they find it more difficult to concentrate for their training in the evening when they have consumed alcohol. Others found the same to be true after they have drunk tea or eaten particular foods. People who take drugs have reported that smoking hashish made concentration more difficult; on the other hand, it has been reported that the consumption of a glass of beer facilitated the exercises.

It should also be considered that the student will not be able to exercise with the same success every day. Still, the more experienced the trainee is, the less will he be side-tracked by internal or external disturbances, in accordance with the Arab proverb: "The dogs bark, but the caravan moves on."

The Cabdriver as Model

The relaxation exercise must, of course, be done in a relaxed position. Our students usually exercise in the so-called cabdriver's position (see illustration). First, straighten your back while seated in a chair, and then slump down. However, there should be no pressure on the stomach—that is, you must not bend too far forward. The head hangs loosely forward, in some people more loosely than in others.

The hands rest relaxed on the thighs. They must not touch each other for that creates a diversion. The elbows are slightly bent, the legs slightly spread, the calves are at a 90-degree angle to the thighs—that is, both feet are flat on the floor.

The eyelids are closed. Of three thousand students only one preferred to exercise with half-open eyes. The tongue is loose and heavy, the jaws are slack although the mouth need not be open.

The "cabdriver's position" or "active sitting position" can be assumed anywhere. It differs from the passive sitting position in which one leans against the back of the chair.

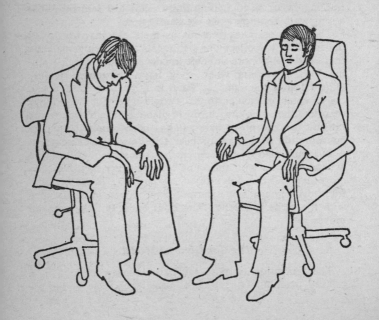

At home you can best do this in an armchair, if possible, resting your head against or on top of the chair back. The arms should rest easily on the arms of the chair. The legs must not be crossed because this interferes with the exercise.

Most people prefer to exercise while lying on their backs and with their heads slightly raised. In this position the elbows are slightly bent, the palms of the hands rest next to the thighs. The person who feels some unpleasant sensations in his chest in this position should place a pillow under his shoulders. The feet, when relaxed, should point slightly outward—if they point directly up, you are not relaxed.

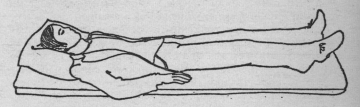

Swaybacked people will have to elevate their knees with two blankets in order to lie in relaxed fashion. Not everyone finds it easy to exercise while lying on his back.

In almost every course students ask whether they can exercise in the position in which they go to sleep. Some, for various physical reasons, prefer to go to sleep while lying on their right sides, and naturally they may do their exercises in that position too. Some people even succeed in exercising while lying on their stomachs. Progress will be slower if the position is frequently varied. The novice especially should always do his exercises in the same position.

Relaxation as an Accomplishment

The successful switch from tension to relaxation determines whether we feel well. The person gripped by physical tension and cramped muscles will also be psychologically cramped, and his relation to the world around him will also be beset with tension.

Tensions are always part of life. But today it seems to

be more difficult to relax than ever before. And it also seems that we cope less well with tensions than our ancestors did.

There is no life without tension. Yet people yearn for it, and whether they call it paradise or utopia or happiness, they are willing to take any shortcut to get there, whether with the help of drugs or even by hurting others.

Everyone reacts differently to tension states. But every sickness also leads to an increase in tension that can have physical, psychological, or social effects. We all know people whose constant state of nervousness irritates us; such people are in a permanent state of excessive tension.

Many people wear a "mask"—they are, in other words, in a permanent state of psychic tension. Tense people have constant muscle spasms. Wilhelm Reich assumed that every "mask" resulted in specific muscle spasms, a regular "muscle armor." Such spasms can be eased by special massages and relaxation exercises, and even the "mask" will be somewhat influenced by these. The well-known connections between psyche and body have been compressed by Julius Fast into the short formula "The body is the message." The body expresses and exhibits what is occurring secretly inside.

Although the ability to relax is normally present, the necessary relaxation of tension often is not. To borrow an image from the world of sports, modern man finds himself perpetually in a state of preparing to jump—but he rarely jumps. As long as twenty years ago the medical journalist J. D. Ratcliff suggested that excessive tension killed more people than any other force endangering our lives. In other words, lack of relaxation kills us.

Dynamic exercises—peaceful walks, rhythmic dancing, relaxing calisthenics—lead naturally to relaxation. Relaxation can also be produced by planned interruptions and changes in activities—by switching from work to hobbies.

The relaxation method inherent in Autogenic Training— "concentrative self-relaxation"—is literally made to order for modern man constantly suffering under the pressure of time, and he should use it in his own self-interest. In relationship to AT, relaxation is actually an accomplishment, for its practice demands character and stamina. Moreover, it contributes to the maturation of the personality.

By turning to his own body, the student learns not only

that he has a body but also that he *is* body. According to Schultz, the student must "slip passively into the physical experience of his body." You must "transport" yourself into the organ you wish to influence. This has nothing to do with the will, for autosuggestion must take place without the exertion of the will and its consequent interference.

Violation of this principle may produce paradoxical effects. Let us consider the process of falling asleep. Anyone who absolutely wants to fall asleep, and tries to force this, will generally make it more difficult, if not impossible, for himself to fall asleep.

Some students find it difficult to distinguish between concentration—that is, the attempt to focus on certain ideas—and the personal will that is always related to active tension. The student's complete abandonment to the content of the formulae he uses in his exercises is in a way a form of self-abandonment, of forgetting himself. It guarantees the success of the exercise: anyone who can learn to relax during Autogenic Training will become relaxed in general.

MATCHING RELAXATION THERAPIES TO TYPES OF ANXIETY: A PATTERNING APPROACH

RICHARD J. DAVIDSON AND GARY E. SCHWARTZ

(Richard J. Davidson is a doctoral candidate at Harvard University. Gary E. Schwartz, Ph.D., is an associate professor in the Department of Psychology at Yale University. The preparation of this paper was supported in part by the Advanced Research Projects Agency of the Department of Defense and monitored by the Office of Naval Research under Contract N00014-70-C-0350 to the San Diego State University Foundation to GES and by National Science Foundation predoctoral fellowship to RJD. This paper is a revised and abridged version of the paper by Davidson and Schwartz noted in the references at the end. *Editors*.)

A number of authors have recently commented upon the multi-dimensional nature of fear and anxiety (e.g. Hodgson & Rachman, 1974; Lang, 1969). When anxiety is elicited in an individual in response to a stressful event, the quality of feelings aroused in one situation may be different than in another. In addition, some people may experience anxiety in one predominant way, while others might become anxious in a different manner. For example, it is not uncommon for a person who is physically tired and somatically relaxed to lie down, unable to fall asleep because his "mind is racing." This individual is manifesting *cognitive* symptoms of anxiety. On the other hand, *somatic* anxiety is characteristic of the person who complains of bodily tension and autonomic stress without accompanying cognitive symptoms.

Given that these two general forms of anxiety exist,[1] is one relaxation technique more effective than others for alleviating cognitive versus somatic anxiety, and vice versa? A number of clinicians have recently proposed that therapeutic regiments should be tailored to particular symptom configurations or response patterns (e.g. Lazarus, 1973). Such a suggestion is based upon the fact that different therapeutic procedures affect different psychobiological systems. We have proposed that the analogous situation prevails in the analysis of the varieties of relaxation procedures (Davidson and Schwartz, 1976). Specifically, relaxation techniques differ in the degree to which they affect the cognitive versus the somatic system. Furthermore, it is hypothesized that those relaxation procedures which affect primarily somatic processes will be maximally effective in the reduction of somatic anxiety while techniques resulting in changes in cognitive events will most effectively attenuate cognitive anxiety. Insofar as different physiological measures reflect predominantly cognitive versus somatic processes, such measures should be changed predictably by the practice of one versus another type of relaxation. By assessing the specific patterning of physiological processes (cf. Schwartz, 1975) in response to different relaxation techniques, the underlying mechanisms of such practices may be elucidated. The following sections will present a brief description of some commonly employed relaxation techniques which will be followed by a discussion of research illustrating the differences in effects elicited by such practices. Finally, a typology of anxiety will be presented and relaxation techniques hypothesized to be maximally effective in reducing particular configurations of anxiety will be discussed.

Some Common Relaxation Techniques:
A Search for their Underlying Mechanisms.

Progressive Relaxation (PR). PR (see Jacobson, 1938) is probably the most extensively used relaxation technique today. Despite the fact that few researchers or clinicians administer this training for as long as Jacobson (1938) prescribed (up to 200 sessions), the effectiveness of even brief training is well established. This relaxation technique entails the systematic focus of attention on the various gross muscle groups throughout the body. The subject is first instructed to actively tense each group for a few seconds after which he is told to release his muscles and relax. Paul (1969) captures the essence of the technique in his instructions to subjects. He explains, "When I say 'relax,' I want you to immediately let go—to stop tensing—and merely focus your attention on what those muscles feel like as relaxation takes place" (p. 427). This sequence, i.e., tension, release, and attention is systematically applied to the following gross muscle groups: dominant hand and forearm, dominant upper arm, nondominant hand and forearm, nondominant upper arm, forehead, eyes and nose, cheeks and mouth, neck and throat, chest, back, and respiratory muscles, abdomen, dominant upper leg, calf, foot, nondominant upper leg, calf, and foot. Progression to each new muscle group is contingent upon complete relaxation of the prior group. The major emphasis of this technique is on *somatic* relaxation. The tensing of each major muscle group increases the saliency of somatic cues, enabling subjects to passively attend to specific body parts, thus facilitating complete somatic relaxation.

Hypnotic Suggestion. Hypnotic suggestions of relaxation are commonly employed to reduce anxiety (e.g. Barber & Hahn, 1963; Paul, 1969). Hypnotic suggestions of relaxation typically involve the active generation of cognitive behavior. For example, a clinician may suggest to a hypnotized patient that he imagine a calm beach with waves gently rolling on the shore. A number of authors (e.g., Shor, 1959, 1962; Orne, 1959) have postulated that the successful completion of a hypnotic suggestion usually involves an alteration of cognitive orientation. This change primarily involves a shift in attention from the external environment to internally generated *cognitive* activity. In a discussion of the effects of hypnotic suggestion, Spanos (1971) explains that "these suggestions often ask subjects to shift their perspective from the natural attitude to the attitude of fantasizing and then to construct in fantasy or imagination a situation which, if it objectively transpired, would result in the behavioral act performed by the subject when he 'passes' the suggestion" (p. 87). The latter situation may be illustrated by the wording of various standard test suggestions. Rather than simply asking subjects to lower their arms, Form C of the Standard Hypnotic Susceptibility Scale (SHSS) suggests arm heaviness in the following manner: "*Imagine* you are holding something heavy in your hand . . . Now the hand and arm *feel* heavy as if the (imagined) weight were pressing down . . ." (Weitzenhoffer and Hilgard, 1962, p. 17, italics added). It therefore seems evident that an important component in the execution of a hypnotic suggestion is the active generation of imagery with occasional attention to somatic processes. Recent research by other investigators (e.g., Spanos, 1971) confirms the important of this type of cognitive activity in hypnotic suggestion. It should be noted that such a relaxation technique, emphasizing active cognitive self-regulation, will elicit subjective and physiological changes which are different from those following the practice of a somatic procedure.

One might suppose, given the important role of imagery in the hypnotic suggestion process, that individual differences in vividness of imagery should co-vary with hypnotic susceptibility. Sutcliffe, Perry and Sheehan (1970) examined this relationship and found that vividness of imagery (as assessed by a modified form of the Betts Questionnaire Upon Mental Imagery, Sheehan, 1967) was, in fact, significantly related to hypnotizability (as assessed by SHSS Form C, Weitzenhoffer and Hilgard, 1962), especially for males, although the veracity of this relationship has recently been questioned (Perry, 1973).

Autogenic Training. This relaxation technique was developed in the early 1900s by J.H. Schultz, a Berlin neuropsychiatrist (Schultz & Lutke, 1959). The core of the procedure is passive somatic attention. Autogenic training typically involves the subject leaning back in an armchair with his eyes closed in a quiet room. Verbal formulae are introduced (e.g., my right arm is heavy) and the subject is specifically instructed to "passively concentrate" on its repetition. The formulae, which consist of verbal somatic suggestions, are intended to facilitate concentration upon and "mental contact" with the part of the body indicated by the formula (e.g., the right arm). The training begins with the theme of heaviness and the first formula is "My right arm his heavy." The heaviness training is then continued for each extremity. The next group of formulae involve warmth and begin with "My right arm is warm." Following warmth training in all the limbs, the trainee continues with passive concentration on cardiac activity by using the formula "Heartbeat calm and regular." Then follows the respiratory mechanism with "It breathes me," and warmth in the abdominal region "My solar plexus is warm." Finally the last formula, "My forehead is cool," is introduced. It is claimed that between four and ten months are usually needed to establish these exercises effectively (Luthe, 1963).

Since the primary emphasis of autogenic training is upon somatic attention and relaxation, one would predict that its effects would be similar to progressive relaxation and different from hypnotic suggestion. Specifically such a technique should exert its greatest effects upon measures of somatic processes which in turn should not be as greatly affected by hypnotic suggestions of relaxation.

Meditation. Although meditative practices were not originally designed as relaxation techniques, the experience of relaxation is a by-product of most such techniques (e.g. Davidson & Goleman, in press). Although there are important differences among the various meditative traditions (see Goleman, 1972), most forms of meditation share a number of common components, including some form of attentional self-regulation and the production of general autonomic quiescence (see Davidson & Goleman, 1975; in press). In the context of the present paper, what concerns us most is the object of attention during meditation. We propose that meditation involving the generation of cognitive events (such as a mantra in Transcendental Meditation) should elicit greater changes on measures of cognitive processing than meditation upon somatic events (such as attention to breathing or attention to the movements of the belly during breathing). Conversely, somatic meditation should result in greater changes on measures of somatic activation than cognitive meditation.

The mechanisms underlying the relaxation techniques discussed above are further revealed by a consideration of some relevant research. The laboratory findings which have emerged in the study of relaxation provide some empirical support for the classification scheme adopted above. Furthermore, the physiological studies on the nature of relaxation have never been guided by any systematic theoretical structure and various anomalies and unexplained findings may be parsimoniously interpreted within the above outlined scheme.

Relaxation Research: Some Core Physiological Findings

Due to the absence of a theoretical foundation, most investigators studying relaxation have rather haphazardly manipulated various treatment parameters and have looked for changes in physiological and subjective measures. The lack of uniformity sometimes observed in the effects of a procedure on a variety of different parameters does not necessarily indicate the lack of validity of those measures. Rather, it is often indicative of the specificity of effects of particular treatments. For example, one relaxation technique may result in heart rate decrements twice as large as another procedure practiced for the same length of time. Such an observation may indicate that the former procedure is a somatically based technique relative to the latter, since heart rate is a good index of overall somatic activity (see Obrist, Webb, Sutterer, & Howard, 1970). As we will see in the next section, such a somatically based technique may be optimally effective in the reduction of somatic anxiety while a cognitively based technique should result in greater change in cognitive anxiety.

Paul (1969) performed a comparative study of the physiological and subjective effects of progressive relaxation and hypnotic suggestion. Sixty subjects participated in two 1-hour sessions held 1 week apart. They were randomly assigned to one of three conditions: a) brief progressive relaxation; b) hypnotic suggestion (of relaxation); and c) self-relaxation control. Forearm EMG, heart rate, skin conductance level and respiration rate were employed as the physiological dependent measures. To examine subjective effects, subjects were administered the Anxiety Differential (Husek and Alexander, 1963). The data for each session were separately examined.

During session 1, relaxation training produced significant reductions as compared with controls on the Anxiety Differential (AD), EMG, heart rate and respiration rate. Hypnotic suggestion versus controls produced significant decreases on the Anxiety Differential and respiration rate. Progressive relaxation produced significantly greater reductions than hypnosis in heart rate and EMG. Eighty-five percent of the subjects in the progressive relaxation condition demonstrated significant reductions in the relaxed direction on the AD, EMG, heart rate and respiration rate while only 30% of the hypnotic suggestion subjects manifested this change. The results for session 2 again indicate that progressive relaxation produced significant reductions as compared with controls on the Anxiety Differential, EMG, heart rate, and respiration rate. When the hypnosis group was compared with controls, significant reductions were noted on the Anxiety Differential, EMG, heart rate, and respiration rate. Again, progressive relaxation was significantly better than hypnotic suggestion in reducing heart rate and EMG. On the other hand, the results for the skin conductance measure were all nonsignificant in both sessions. In session 2, 70% of the relaxation subjects evidenced significant reduction in the four measures, while only 25% of the hypnotic suggestion subjects evidenced the same degree of change.

It can be inferred from the findings of this study that there are components of the relaxation procedure, absent in hypnotic suggestion, which are responsible for the superior performance of the former group. Paul (1969) suggests that:

> Restricted attention, narrow and monotonous stimulus input, and suggested ease of response were . . . factors common to both relaxation training and hypnotic conditions. The results obtained on the Anxiety Differential suggests that the latter factors in combi-

nation with either direct or indirect suggestions of relaxation, are sufficient to alter the *cognitive* experience
of distress, while the results on physiological measures
suggest that the differential content of stimulus input
and attentional focus were of prime importance in the
alteration of *somatic* responses (p. 435) (italics added).

Paul correctly implicates differences in stimulus input and
attentional focus as being important factors underlying
the differential consequences of progressive relaxation versus hypnotic relaxation. The question that now can be
posed concerns the nature of these differences. What are
the underlying processes in progressive relaxation and hypnotic suggestion that can account for the observed results?

In addition, it is also important to examine the nature
of the dependent variables to determine the modality most
represented by each measure. Hypnotic suggestion, as previously argued, involves the active generation of imagery.
In his instructions to subjects, Paul (1969) explained that
the hypnotic procedure utilizes imagery to induce a state of
deep relaxation. He further suggested to subjects that during
hypnosis, they are to "systematically focus your attention
on a visual image of yourself" (p. 428).

Progressive relaxation, on the other hand, is precisely
antithetical in its process to hypnotic suggestion. As was
previously suggested, this technique involves a somatic attentional focus. Subjects are first instructed to tense a
specific group of muscles, followed by letting go, relaxing
and passively attending to the results of the procedure. It
should be emphasized that subjects in the progressive relaxation procedure do not actively generate relaxation, but
rather relaxation "takes place" and they just passively
attend to how it feels. There is a reduction in efferent commands which allows the subject to more fully attend to the
specific body part to be relaxed, free from the distractions
of the former processes. In summary, then, one can state
that hypnotic suggestion is an active cognitive process while
progressive relaxation is a passive somatic process.

The dependent measures chosen by Paul may also be
classified into primarily somatic-sensitive or cognitive-sen-
sitive variables as was outlined in the previous secton.
Forearm EMG, respiration and heart rate (Obrist, Webb,

Sutterer, and Howard, 1970) are all somatic measures, while skin conductance level (Kilpatrick, 1972) and the Anxiety Differential may reflect more cognitive processes. Since the goal of both relaxation techniques is to effect changes in the somatic system, one's attention must be focused there. Because this was true for the progressive relaxation subjects, one would expect greater changes in the direction of relaxation for this group versus the hypnosis group on somatic dependent measures. In both sessions, progressive relaxation led to greater decrements in heart rate and forearm EMG than hypnotic suggestions, although decrements in respiration rate and on the Anxiety Differential were not significantly different in either session. While not statistically significant, there was a greater decrement in respiration rate for the progressive relaxation versus the hypnosis group in both sessions. Both the progressive relaxation and hypnotic suggestion groups and the control group all manifested decrements in skin conductance level with no significant differences between the three groups. Therefore, it is evident that a relaxation technique that requires somatic attention will result in a greater degree of relaxation when assessed by somatic measures than a technique that requires cognitive attention.

It is important to note that the two variables reflecting primarily cognitive activity did not differentiate between the two relaxation techniques. One might ask why progressive relaxation, a somatic procedure, also led to increases in cognitive relaxation. It is probable that the phenomenon in question is multiply-determined and more than one explanation is possible. A number of tentative hypotheses, none mutually exclusive, may be offered. To begin with, neither the Anxiety Differential nor skin conductance level are "pure" cognitive measures. The Anxiety Differential has some items which are somatic in nature, although there are a greater number of cognitive items. Although recent research on electrodermal activity suggests that skin conductance level (as distinct from skin conductance responses) primarily reflects cognitive activity (Kilpatrick, 1972) these data are by no means conclusive. Therefore, the first hypothesis is that these measures could have reflected changes in both cognitive *and* somatic behavior, so that it is possible for the somatic changes induced by progressive relaxation to be reflected in the Anxiety Differential and skin conductance. The second, and probably more tenable hypothesis, is that *processes occurring in a given mode strongly affect that same mode, although they also influence other modes to a lesser degree.* In other words, if an individual employs a somatic relaxation technique and becomes very relaxed, this relaxation will partially generalize to the cognitive sphere as well.

A number of other investigators have performed comparative studies of the physiological concomitants of different relaxation procedures. For example, Langen (1969) found that autogenic training elicited greater increases than hypnotic suggestion in heat conveyance, which is a measure of peripheral vasodilatation. Langen's data are clearly in agreement with those obtained by Paul (1969). Both studies compared hypnotic suggestion—an active cognitive process—with techniques that require passive somatic attention. Both experiments revealed that the active generation of internal cognitive behavior was not as effective as passive somatic attention in altering cardiovascular processes. The Paul (1969) study did demonstrate, however, that there were no differences between progressive relaxation and hypnotic suggestion in the alteration of cognitive behavior.

There exist numerous additional findings in areas other than relaxation per se which have bearing on the basic cognitive-somatic distinction discussed herein (e.g., Bell and Schwartz, 1973; Kurie and Mordkoff, 1970). These studies suggest, not surprisingly, that when subjects are asked to self-regulate somatic activity, greater changes are seen on dependent measures which reflect somatic processes (e.g. heart rate) than on other types of measures and vice versa. It should be emphasized that such a distinction (i.e., cognitive versus somatic) is at the most molar level of behavior and further, more refined subdivisions may be made within each of the two larger modes. For example, the general class of imagery may be differentiated into its modality-specific components, i.e., visual imagery, auditory imagery, etc. Importantly, research suggests that the generation of imagery in a particular modality will inhibit the perception of stimuli in that modality more than in others (e.g. Segal and Fusella, 1970). These data have bearing on the mode-specific treatment of anxiety which will be described below.

Cognitive and Somatic Anxiety and Relaxation Mode

A number of writers have recently commented upon cognitive and somatic distinctions in anxiety (e.g., Corah, 1964; Eysenck, 1961; Barratt, 1972). For example, Barratt (1972) performed an item analysis of anxiety items from a large battery of popular scales. This analysis "indicated two major subsets: (1) awareness of somatic changes, for example, I blush often or I am often aware of my heart beating; (2) conscious awareness of unpleasant feelings about self or external stimuli, for example, I frequently find myself worrying about something . . ." (Barratt, 1972, p. 202). The latter factor clearly represents the cognitive symptoms of anxiety. These two distinct manifestations of anxiety may also be represented quantitatively by a ratio of cognitive/somatic symptoms or other similar ratios. For example, Corah (1964) has computed a "proportion of somatic anxiety score" which was obtained for each patient by subtracting the number of cognitive symptoms from the number of somatic symptoms and dividing by the total number of symptoms.

If we conceive of cognitive and somatic anxiety as reflecting mode-specific intra-organismic states, it follows, in the context of the principles previously developed, that different relaxation techniques, i.e., cognitive vs. somatic, will be more effective in reducing same mode vs. other mode anxiety. As an illustration, let us return to an example offered in the introduction. An extreme case of high cognitive-low somatic anxiety occurs when an individual is somatically tired and lying down, but can't fall asleep because his mind is "racing." Assuming that this individual's body is relatively relaxed, it is clear that a cognitive/somatic anxiety ratio would yield a result greater than 1. In this situation, the most efficient type of relaxation would be a cognitive procedure which would reduce *unwanted* cognitive activity (hence the age-old procedure of visualizing and counting sheep).

Table 1 presents a 2x2 table with the following four combinations of anxiety represented in each cell: a) low cognitive-low somatic; b) low cognitive-high somatic; c)

TABLE 1.

Cognitive and somatic components of anxiety and associated relaxation techniques hypothesized to reduce such anxiety.

| | | SOMATIC ANXIETY | |
		LOW	HIGH
COGNITIVE ANXIETY	LOW	Meditation	Progressive Relaxation Hatha Yoga Walking
	HIGH	Reading Watching Television Playing Chess	Dancing Active Sports (e.g., tennis, football)

high cognitive-low somatic; and d) high cognitive-high somatic. Within each cell, a number of techniques and/or activities are presented which theoretically should be maximally effective in eliciting "relaxation" for the particular configuration of anxiety represented by each cell. A number of general characteristics of this table will first be discussed, followed by a more detailed explanation of the hypothesized relationships.

The low cognitive anxiety column subjectively represents a lack of unwanted cognitive intrusions. Because of this absence, attention is not distracted by activity in the cognitive sphere. Hence, every activity and technique in this column has the following important characteristic in common: none requires sustained active generation of cognitive behavior. In other words, since the cognitive mode is already relatively quiescent, it is not necessary to utilize a technique which directly inhibits cognitive intrusions.

The high cognitive anxiety column represents, on the other hand, an abundance of unwanted cognitive activity which requires a relaxation technique that will directly inhibit these cognitive distractions. All of the techniques and activities in the high cognitive anxiety column require the active generation of cognitive behavior or, in the case of television, the total engagement and involvement of the entire perceptual-cognitive system. According to the principle outlined in the previous section, it can be argued that *active* cognitive generation, either predominantly self-initiated as in chess, or predominantly externally initiated as in television, will most effectively inhibit cognitive intrusions.

A parallel analysis can be applied to the rows. In the low somatic anxiety row, every activity and technique requires little or no active somatic generation, while in the high somatic anxiety row, every technique and activity requires the active generation of somatic behavior.

A closer inspection of Table 1 reveals a number of more specific hypotheses concerning anxiety-relaxation relationships. The low cognitive-low somatic anxiety cell suggests that only those individuals, at those moments experiencing generally low anxiety in both modes, will choose meditation as a form of relaxation. Additionally, one can deduce that these techniques (e.g., TM® and Zen) would not be totally effective for *generally* anxious individuals (i.e., those manifesting high cognitive and high somatic anxiety).

We have placed meditation in this cell because of evidence which suggests that people with elevated levels of anxiety will not, at least initially, be benefitted by meditation and will be less likely to persist in their practice. Otis (1973) has performed a longitudinal study of meditators and found that those initiates who practiced regularly for more than 12 months characterized themselves as less anxious, more calm and peaceful than those who dropped out before 12 months, *before* either group had begun meditation.

The low cognitive-high somatic anxiety cell indicates that techniques demanding somatic attention with little or no cognitive generation are effective in reducing this pattern of anxiety. A curious clinical observation is worth noting here. Many teachers and practitioners of meditation have commented upon the importance of relaxing the body and reducing somatic anxiety (usually through the practice of hatha yoga) *before* commencing intensive meditation (e.g., Satchidananda, 1970). Due to the relative passivity of most meditation procedures, distracting cognitive and somatic anxiety must first be reduced through the utilization of more active, mode-specific techniques.

The procedures included in the high cognitive-low somatic cell all require active cognitive generation with little somatic attention. It is hypothesized that these complex behaviors demand the active generation of cognitive events which serve to inhibit ongoing unwanted cognitive activity, i.e., cognitive anxiety (see Csikszenthmihalyi, 1974; 1975). It is particularly intriguing that most of these activities are among those most frequently reported as being related to increased susceptibility to hypnosis (J. Hilgard, 1970, 1972). Hilgard (1970) has found that involvement in reading and drama is significantly related to hypnotizability. These activities and procedures all have the same common theme at their core: the sustained involvement in active generation of cognitive behavior.

Finally, the last cell—high cognitive-high somatic—includes activities that require both active cognitive and somatic generation. These activities are among the most attentionally demanding behaviors in which individuals typically engage. A lapse of attention in either mode in a game of tennis, for example, will have detrimental consequences. One may question how intensive physical activity can be relaxing, particularly in light of Pitts' (Pitts and McClure, 1967; Pitts, 1969; Pitts, 1971) suggestion that lactate, an exercise metabolite, can provoke anxiety symptoms and attacks in anxiety neurotics and in normal persons under stress. Pitts' theorizing and data have been recently criticized by a number of investigators (e.g., Ackerman and Sacher, 1974; Grosz and Farmer, 1969; Levitt, 1972; Morgan, 1973). Grosz and Farmer (1969) present convincing evidence suggesting that the anxiety producing substance is not lactate, but rather sodium bicarbonate. However, perhaps most damaging is a series of studies by Morgan and his colleagues (Morgan, 1973; Morgan, Roberts, Brand and Feinerman, 1970; Morgan, Roberts and Feinerman, 1971) which convincingly demonstrated that physical exercise consistently led to significant decrements in state anxiety among both normal and high anxious subjects. These data lend empirical support to the general hypothesis that intensive physical exercise can lead to decrements in anxiety, probably by inhibiting unwanted cognitive and somatic behavior, plus producing a fatigue state which further reduced such behavior (Grim, 1972).

Summary and Conclusions

A process-oriented patterning conception of relaxation and related states was presented. It was argued that different relaxation techniques activate different major modes or systems and it was suggested that the effects of particular relaxation techniques can be meaningfully understood only after determining the type of dependent variable employed (i.e., it is more sensitive to cognitive or somatic processes?). The utilization of these principles in the examination of some core findings in the empirical literature on relaxation rendered a number of anomalous findings understandable. Data were presented demonstrating that progressive relaxation—a somatic technique—was significantly superior to hypnotic relaxation—a cognitive technique—on a number of somatic measures, while the results on a cognitive measure yielded no significant differences. Similar results for other relaxation procedures were also described. Finally, the principles that were previously developed were applied to an examination of anxiety. It was demonstrated that the cognitive and somatic contributions to anxiety can be meaningfully separated and a model was presented which matched specific relaxation techniques to specific anxiety patterns on the basis of their underlying processes. Clearly additional research is needed to test and clarify the numerous hypotheses presented.

A number of empirical and practical conclusions emerge from this kind of analysis. On the empirical side, it is suggested that various meditative and relaxation practices can be understood and investigated by careful analysis of the underlying cognitive, somatic, and attentional processes that are brought into play. Current theories of emotion (e.g., Schacter, 1970) and self-regulation of consciousness (e.g., Schwartz, 1975) and recent research on delay of gratification (e.g., Mischel, 1974) utilize a multi-process or pattern approach. This conceptual scheme emphasizing *interactions* of factors is consistent with present neurophysiological theories of perception (Pribram, 1971), memory (John, 1972) and consciousness (Shallice, 1972; Sperry, 1969). Although we have emphasized cognitive and somatic factors as two general modes, this broad classification by definition is an oversimplification since each can be meaningfully broken into subcomponents (e.g., visual, auditory, and kinesthetic imagery). Nonetheless, we believe that two general principles pertaining to relaxation and anxiety reduction will still apply: (1) that self-regulation of behavior (including voluntary focusing of attention) in a given mode will reduce (or inhibit) unwanted activity in that specific mode, and (2) that self-regulation of behavior in a given mode may, to a lesser degree, reduce unwanted activity in other modes.[2]

The importance of considering patterns of underlying processes must be underscored. The theory suggests that the age-proven procedure of visualizing *and* counting sheep to fall asleep when one's mind is racing succeeds because it effectively blocks both unwanted visual *and* auditory imagery at the same time. Similarly, it may be hypothesized that forms of Zen meditation which require that the person count his breaths or say a mantra in synchrony with breathing are particularly effective because they simultaneously attenuate both cognitive and somatic components of anxiety. It follows that a 2x2 classification representing high and low cognitive and somatic anxiety is also an oversimplification, for it represents only a first-order breakdown. For example, the present theory suggests that within the low cognitive-low somatic category, a meditation procedure based upon the self-generation of cognition (e.g., a mantra technique such as Transcendental Meditation) will be relatively more effective for reducing cognitive components of anxiety than a meditation practice based upon the passive attentional focusing upon somatic events, which should be relatively more effective for reducing the somatic components of anxiety.

From a clinical point of view, it would seem valuable to assess anxiety in a more systematic way so as to uncover the specific modes in which the unwanted behavior is occurring. The theory implies that then, and only then, will it be possible to determine which relaxation technique (i.e., which mode-specific tactic(s)) should be most effective in reducing anxiety for a given patient in a given state. Although clearly in need of additional experimental tests, this general hypothesis must be tempered by the fact that also important is the patient's motivation to faithfully practice any given technique (e.g., Schwartz, 1973). As in all forms of psychological and medical treatment, isolating the most powerful procedure is not enough; the procedure must also be acceptable to the patient if it is going to be used most effectively. It might also be mentioned that a new direction in therapy may be to teach people to recognize in themselves when they are experiencing what kinds of anxiety, and how best to eliminate it, since it is conceivable that people differ in their ability to best fit a type of relaxation to the bio-behavioral need (e.g., how does one learn to select a slow, quieting passage to listen to versus a fast, loud passage which activates foot-tapping and dancing?).

In a review of laboratory studies on desensitization, Lang (1969) once described fear as a "loosely woven fabric of responses, with many edges where an unravelling process may be initiated" (p. 190). We would suggest that the same applies to the concept of relaxation as used in every-day language. Central to any concept of relaxation is the attempt at eliminating unwanted behavior; what the behavior is and how the person goes about avoiding or eliminating it can vary greatly. However, it is possible to consider what relaxation would be if it occurred in all modes simultaneously. This, we suggest, is what the final end point of many (but not all) eastern and western relaxation techniques is—a reduction in self-generated cognitive, somatic and attentional behavior (i.e., attentional receptivity rather than active focusing of attention). It seems likely that only under such circumstances is it possible for the deep, integrated "hypometabolic" state described by Wallace and Benson (1972) and renamed "the relaxation response" (Benson, 1975) to occur.

NOTES

1. It should be noted that such a split is at the most basic of levels. Further subdivisions have recently been made (see Davidson and Schwartz, in press) and will ultimately be necessary in any complete account of the nature of anxiety.

2. The converse of this principle is that reductions in self-generated behavior in one mode may result in an increase in (or release of) spontaneous behavior in another mode. Hence, deep muscle relaxation with biofeedback may be accompanied by increases in spontaneous thoughts and imagery (e.g., Green, Walters, Green and Murphy, 1969; Stoyva, 1973). This phenomenon of spontaneous release of cognitive events concomitant with reductions in somatic activity has been recog-

nized by investigators of autogenic training and has been termed "autogenic discharge" (Gorton, 1959; Luthe, 1963).

REFERENCES

Ackerman, S.H. and Sacher, R.J. The lactate theory of anxiety: A review and reevaluation. *Psychosomatic Medicine*, 1974, *36*, 69–81.

Barber, T.X., and Han, K.W. Hypnotic induction and "relaxation": An experimental study. *Archives of General Psychiatry*, 1963, *8*, 295–300.

Barrett, E.S. Anxiety and impulsiveness: Toward a neuropsychological model. In C.D. Spielberger (Ed.), *Anxiety: Current Trends in Theory and Research, Vol. 1.* New York: Academic Press, 1972.

Bell, I.R., and Schwartz, G.E. Cognitive and somatic mechanisms in voluntary control of heart rate. In Shapiro, T.X. Barber, L. V. DiCara, J. Kamiya, N.E. Miller and J. Stoyva (Eds.), *Biofeedback and Self-Control, 1972.* Chicago: Aldine, 1972 (Abstract).

Benson, H. *The Relaxation Response.* New York: William Morrow, 1975.

Corah, N.L. Neuroticism and extraversion in the MMPI: Empirical validation and exploration. *British Journal of Social and Clinical Psychology*, 1964, *3*, 168–174.

Czikszenthmihalyi, M. *Flow: Studies of Enjoyment.* Unpublished PHS Grant Report, 1974.

Czikszenthmihalyi, M. *Beyond Boredom and Anxiety.* San Francisco: Jossey-Bass, 1975.

Davidson, R.J. and Goleman, D.J. The role of attention in meditation and hypnosis: A psychobiological model of transformations of consciousness. Paper presented at the Society for Clinical and Experimental Hypnosis, Chicago, October, 1975.

Davidson, R.J. and Goleman, D.J. Attentional and affective concomitants of meditation: A cross-sectional study. *Journal of Abnormal Psychology*, in press.

Davidson, R.J. and Schwartz, G.E. The psychobiology of relaxation and related states: A multi-process theory. In D.I. Mostofsky (Ed.) *Behavior Control and the Modification of Physiological Processes.* New York: Prentice-Hall, in press.

Eysenck, H.J. Classification and the problems of diagnosis. In H.J. Eysenck (Ed.), *Handbook of Abnormal Psychology.* New York: Basic Books, 1961.

Goleman, D. The Buddha on meditation and states of consciousness, Part II: a typology of meditation techniques. *Journal of Transpersonal Psychology*, 1972, *4*, 151–210.

Green, E.E., Walters, D.E., Green, A.M., and Murphy, G. Feedback technique for deep relaxation. *Psychophysiology*, 1969, *6*, 371–377.

Grim, P.F. Relaxation therapies and neurosis: A central fatigue interpretation. *Psychosomatics*, 1972, *13*, 363–370.

Grosz, H.J., and Farmer, B.B. Blood lactate in the development of anxiety symptoms: A critical examination of Pitts and McClure's hypothesis and experimental study. *Archives of General Psychiatry*, 1969, *21*, 611–619.

Hilgard, J.R. *Personality and Hypnosis: A Study of Imaginative Involvement*. Chicago: University of Chicago Press, 1970.

Hilgard, J.R. Evidence for a development-interactive theory of hypnotic susceptibility. In E. Fromm and R.E. Shor (Eds.), *Hypnosis: Research Developments and Perspectives*. Chicago: Aldine, 1972.

Hodgson, R. and Rachman, R. II. Desynchrony in measures of fear. *Behavior Research and Therapy*, 1974, *12*, 319–326.

Husek, T.R., and Alyxander, S. The effectiveness of the Anxiety Differential in examination situations. *Educational and Psychological Measurement*, 1963, *23*, 309–318.

Jacobson, E. *Progressive Relaxation*. Chicago: University of Chicago Press, 1938. (2nd edition).

John, E.R. Switchboard versus statistical theories of learning and memory. *Science*, 1972, *177*, 850–864.

Kilpatrick, D.G. Differential responsiveness of two electrodermal indices to psychological stress and performance of a complex cognitive task. *Psychophysiology*, 1972, *9*, 218–226.

Kurie, G.D. and Mordkoff, A.M. Effects of brief sensory deprivation and somatic concentration on two measures of field dependence. *Perceptual and Motor Skills*, 1970, *31*, 683–687.

Lang, P. The mechanics of desensitization and the laboratory study of human fear. In C.M. Franks (Ed.), *Behavior Therapy: Appraisal and Status*. New York: McGraw-Hill, 1969.

Langen, D. Peripheral changes in blood circulation during autogenic training and hypnosis (Results of experimental research). In L. Chertok (Ed.), *Psychophysiological Mechanisms of Hypnosis*. Berlin: Springer-Verlag, 1969.

Lazarus, A.A. Multimodal behavior therapy: Treating the "basic id." *Journal of Nervous and Mental Disease*, 1973, *156*, 404–411.

Levitt, E.E. A brief commentary on the "psychiatric breakthrough" with emphasis on the hematology of anxiety. In C.D. Spielberger (Ed.), *Anxiety: Current Trends in Theory and Research. Volume 1*. New York: Academic Press, 1972.

Luthe, W. Autogenic training: Method, research and application in medicine. *American Journal of Psychotherapy*, 1963, *17*, 174–195.

Mischel, W. Processes in delay of gratification. In L. Berkowitz (Ed.), *Advances in Social Psychology. Volume 7*. New York: Academic Press, 1974, 249–292.

Morgan, W.P. Influence of acute physical activity on state anxiety. Paper presented at the Annual Meeting of the National College Physical Education Association for Men, January 9, 1973.

Morgan, W.P., Roberts, J.A., and Feinerman, A.D. Psychologic Psychological effect of chronic physical activity. *Medicine and Science in Sports*, 1970, *2*, 213–217.

Morgan, W.P., Robert, J.A., and Feinerman, A.D. Psychologic effect of acute physical exercise. *Archives of Physical Medicine and Rehabilitation*, 1971, *52*, 422–425.

Obrist, P.A., Webb, R.A., Sutterer, J.R., and Howard, J.L. The cardio-somatic relationship: Some reformulations. *Psychophysiology*, 1970, *6*, 569–587.

Orne, M.T. The nature of hypnosis: Artifact and essence. *Journal of Abnormal and Social Psychology*, 1959, *58*, 277–299.

Otis, L.S. The psychobiology of meditation: Some psychological changes. Paper presented at the 81st annual meeting of the American Psychological Association, Montreal, August, 1973.

Paul, G.L. Physiological effects of relation training and hypnotic suggestion. *Journal of Abnormal Psychology*, 1969, *74*, 425–437.

Perry, C. Imagery, fantasy and hypnotic susceptibility: A multidimensional approach. *Journal of Personality and Social Psychology*, 1973, *26*, 217–221.

Pitts, F.N., Jr. The biochemistry of anxiety. *Scientific American*, 1969, *220*, 69–75.

Pitts, F.J., Jr. Biochemical factors in anxiety neurosis. *Behavioral Sciences*, 1971, *16*, 82–91.

Pitts, F.N., Jr., and McClure, J.N., Jr. Lactate metabolism in anxiety neurosis. *New England Journal of Medicine*, 1967, *277*, 1329–1336.

Pribram, K.H. *Languages of the Brain*. Englewood Cliffs, New Jersey: Prentice-Hall, 1971.

Satchidananda, Y.S.S. *Integral Yoga Hatha*. New York: Holt, Rinehart and Winston, 1970.

Schachter, S. The assumption of identity and peripheralist-centralist controversies in motivation and emotion. In M. Arnold (Ed.), *Feelings and Emotions*. New York: Academic Press, 1970.

Schultz, J.H., and Luthe, W. *Autogenic Training: A Psychophysiological Approach to Psychotherapy*. New York: Grune and Stratton, 1959.

Schwartz, G.E. Biofeedback as therapy: Some theoretical and practical issues. *American Psychologist*, 1973, *28*, 666–673.

Schwartz, G.E. Biofeedback, self-regulation and the patterning of physiological processes. *American Scientist*, 1975, *63*, 314–324.

Segal, S.J., and Fusella, V. Influence of imaged pictures and sounds on detection of auditory and visual signals. *Journal of Experimental Psychology*, 1970, *83*, 458–464.

Shallice, T. Dual functions of consciousness. *Psychological Review*, 1972, *79*, 383–393

Sheehan, P.W. A shortened form of Betts' Questionnaire Upon Mental Imagery. *Journal of Clinical Psychology*, 1967, *23*, 386–389.

Shor, R.E. Hypnosis and the concept of the generalized reality-orientation. *American Journal of Psychotherapy*, 1959, *13*, 582–602.

Shor, R.E. Three dimensions of hypnotic depth. *International Journal of Clinical and Experimental Hypnosis*, 1962, *10*, 23–38.

Spanos, N.P. Goal-directed fantasy and the performance of hypnotic test suggestions. *Psychiatry*, 1971, *34*, 86–96.

Sperry, R.W. A modified concept of consciousness. *Psychological Review*, 1969, *76*, 532–536.

Stoyva, J. Biofeedback techniques and the conditions for hallucinatory activity. In F.J. McGuigan and R.A. Schoonover (Eds.), *The Psychophysiology of Thinking*. New York: Academic Press, 1973.

Sutcliffe, J.P., Perry C.W., and Sheehan, P.W. Relation of some aspects of imagery and fantasy to hypnotic susceptibility. *Journal of Abnormal Psychology*, 1970, *76*, 279–287.

Wallace, R.K., and Benson, H. The physiology of meditation. *Scientific American*, 1972, *226*, 84–90.

Weitzenhoffer, A.M., and Hilgard, E.R. *Stanford Hypnotic Susceptibility Scale, Form C*. Palo Alto, California: Consulting Psychologists Press, 1962.

AFTERWORD: IF I COULD LIVE IT OVER . . .

NADINE STAIR

(This delightful perspective of life was written at age 85. *Editors.*)

If I had to live my life over again, I'd dare to make more mistakes next time.

I'd relax.

I would limber up.

I would be sillier than I have been this trip.

I would take fewer things seriously.

I would take more chances.

I would take more trips. I would climb more mountains, swim more rivers.

I would eat more ice cream and less beans.

I would perhaps have more actual troubles, but I'd have fewer imaginary ones.

You see, I'm one of those people who live seriously and sanely hour after hour, day after day.

Oh, I've had my moments. And if I had it to do over again, I'd have more of them.

In fact, I'd try to have nothing else, just moments, one after another, instead of living so many years ahead of each day.

I've been one of those persons who never goes anywhere without a thermometer, a hot water bottle, a raincoat and a parachute.

If I had it to do again, I would travel lighter than I have.

If I had to live my life over, I would start barefoot earlier in the spring and stay that way later in fall.

I would go to more dances.

I would ride more merry-go-rounds.

I would pick more daisies.

APPENDIXES

RELAXATION AND RELATED STATES:

A Bibliography of Psychological and Physiological Research

RICHARD J. DAVIDSON AND GARY E. SCHWARTZ

(This unpublished bibliography is complete through September 1973. A final section listing foreign language references has been deleted here. Preparation of this review was supported in part by the Advance Research Projects Agency of the Department of Defense and monitored by the Office of Naval Research under Contract N00014-70-C-0350 to the San Diego State University Foundation to G. E. Schwartz. The authors especially thank Sharon Cronan for her help in completing the bibliography. *Editors*.)

Introduction

The concept of relaxation has had a long and varied history. In the early part of the century, Edmund Jacobson (1929) introduced a form of therapy based on muscular quiescence, known as progressive relaxation. American interest in the topic of relaxation waned during the 1940s and early 1950s. It was not until the introduction of systematic desensitization therapy (in which progressive relaxation played an important role) by Wolpe in 1958 that American interest in this topic was once again renewed.

During the past decade, research in relaxation has received an increasing amount of attention. The existing literature on relaxation and related states is extremely diverse and the foundations upon which this body of literature rests range from the age-old meditative disciplines of the East to the contemporary research on behavior therapy. Equally varied are the journals where this literature has been published. The data on Western relaxation techniques is mostly found in widely available journals devoted to psychotherapy and abnormal behavior. The Eastern literature on relaxation is more scattered and appears in both American and foreign journals. Because of this inherent diversity in relaxation research, a broadly-based bibliography surveying the scientific literature on this topic was deemed valuable.

The bibliography grew out of a search for background material on relaxation and related states and techniques for their induction. A primary concern in surveying the literature was to determine if relaxation can enhance human performance, and if so, which techniques might be most appropriate for a given set of conditions. The definition of relaxation employed in selecting these references was quite broad and inclusive of all procedures related to low-arousal states and their effects on all types of behavior and experience. An effort was made to restrict the bibliography to experimental or quasi-experimental studies and empirically derived theoretical papers. However, some references reflecting a more philosophical approach, particularly in the meditation section, were included to provide background sources on the various meditative techniques.

The period surveyed in this bibliography generally ranges from 1960 through the first part of 1973. Selected references before 1960 were included where these were judged to represent classic contributions to the literature (e.g., Edmund Jacobson's 1929 contribution, *Progressive Relaxation*).[1] Selected papers on yoga and meditation were included when they were centrally concerned with the cultivation and/or effects of low arousal, hypometabolic states. Additional citations on meditation can be found in a recent bibliography on the subject compiled by Timmons and Kamiya (1970).

In an attempt to impose some organization on this literature, the bibliography is divided into the following content areas:

I. Effects of Relaxation *per se* on Psychological and Physiological Processes.
II. Role of Relaxation in Systematic Desensitization.
III. Relaxation and Biofeedback.
IV. Relaxation and Hypnotic Suggestion.

---

[1] A complete bibliography of Jacobson's work prior to 1969 can be found in Jacobson (1964).

The miscellaneous section includes papers that bear on some aspect of relaxation but are not centrally concerned with this topic. If a particular reference fell in more than one category, a judgment was made as to the most appropriate section; no reference is listed more than once. Titles of foreign language articles are translated into English (and are indicated by enclosure in parentheses) and the original foreign title was also included when available. Not all articles were available for inspection.

I. Effects of Relaxation per se on Psychological and Physiological Processes

Burns, J.M., & Ascough, J.C. A physiological comparison of two approaches to relaxation and anxiety induction. *Behavior Therapy*, 1971, *2*, 170–176.

Chaney, D.S., & Andreasen, L. Relaxation and neuromuscular control and changes in mental performance under induced tension. *Perceptual and Motor Skills*, 1972, *34*, 677–678.

Davidson, P.O., & Hiebert, S.F. Relaxation training, relaxation instruction, and repeated exposure to a stressor film. *Journal of Abnormal Psychology*, 1971, *78*, 154–159.

Edelman, R.I. Effects of progressive relaxation on autonomic processes. *Journal of Clinical Psychology*, 1970, *26*, 421–425.

Epstein, L.H., & Kotses, H. Effects of brief relaxation training on skin resistance. *Catalog of Selected Documents in Psychology*, 1972, *2*, 59.

Freeling, N.W. The psychophysiological effects of brief relaxation training: A test of the maximal habituation hypothesis. *Dissertation Abstracts International*, 1972, *32*, 4856–4857.

Jacobson, E. Voluntary relaxation of the esophagus. *American Journal of Physiology*, 1925, *72*, 387–394.

Jacobson, E. *Progressive Relaxation*. Chicago: University of Chicago Press, 1929.

Jacobson, E. Electrical measurements concerning muscular contraction (tonus) and the cultivation of relaxation in man. *American Journal of Physiology*, 1934, *107*, 230–248.

Jacobson, E. *Progressive Relaxation*. Chicago: University of Chicago Press, 1938. (2nd ed.)

Jacobson, E. Neuromuscular controls in man: Methods of self direction in health and disease. *American Journal of Physiology*, 1955, *68*, 549–561.

Jacobson, E. *You Must Relax*. New York: McGraw-Hill, 1957.

Jacobson, E. *Anxiety and Tension Control*. Philadelphia: Lippincott, 1964.

Jacobson, E. Electrophysiology of mental activities and introduction to the psychological process of thinking. In F.J. McGuigan & R.A. Schoonover (Eds.), *The Psychophysiology of Thinking*. New York: Academic Press, 1973, pp. 3–31.

Johnson, D.T., & Spielberger, C.D. The effects of relaxation training and the passage of time on measures of state and trait anxiety. *Journal of Clinical Psychology*, 1968, *24*, 20–23.

Lader, M.H., & Mathews, A.M. Comparison of methods of relaxation using physiological measures. *Behaviour Research & Therapy*, 1970, *8*, 331–337.

Lader, M.H., & Mathews, A.M. Electromyographic studies of tension. *Journal of Psychosomatic Research*, 1971, *15*, 479–486.

Mathews, A.M., & Gelder, M.G. Psycho-physiological investigations of brief relaxation training. *Journal of Psychosomatic Research*, 1969, *13*, 1–12.

Simpson, D.D., Dansereau, D.F., & Giles, G.J. A preliminary evaluation of physiological and behavioral effects of self-directed relaxation. *Catalog of Selected Documents in Psychology*, 1972, *2*, 59.

Stoudenmire, J. Effects of muscle relaxation training on state and trait anxiety in introverts and extroverts. *Journal of Personality and Social Psychology*, 1972, *24*, 273–275.

Straughan, J.H., & Dufort, W.H. Task difficulty, relaxation, and anxiety level during verbal learning and recall. *Journal of Abnormal Psychology*, 1969, *74*, 621–624.

Timmons, B., Salamy, J., Kamiya, J., & Girton, D. Abdominal-thoracic respiratory movements and levels of arousal. *Psychonomic Science*, 1972, *27*, 173–175.

Wilson, A., & Wilson, A.S. Psychophysiological and learning correlates of anxiety and induced muscle relaxation. *Psychophysiology*, 1970, *6*, 740–748.

Wolpe, J., & Flood, J. The effect of relaxation on the galvanic skin response to repeated phobic stimuli in ascending order. *Journal of Behavior Therapy and Experimental Psychiatry*, 1970, *1*, 195–200.

Yorkston, N.J., & Sergeant, H.G.S. Simple method of relaxation. *Lancet*, 1962, *2*, 1319–1321.

II. Role of Relaxation in Systematic Desensitization

Aponte, J.F., & Aponte, C.E. Group preprogrammed systematic desensitization without the simultaneous presentation of aversive scenes with relaxation training. *Behaviour Research and Therapy*, 1971, *9*, 337–346.

Brooker, R.E. The effect of immediate feedback during relaxation training on the process of systematic desensitization. *Dissertation Abstracts International*, 1972, *32*, 4853.

Cooke, G. Evaluation of the efficacy of the components of reciprocal inhibition psychotherapy. *Journal of Abnormal Psychology*, 1968, *73*, 464–467.

Davison, G.C. Systematic desensitization as a counter-conditioning process. *Journal of Abnormal Psychology*, 1968, *73*, 91–99.

Davison, G.C. A procedural critique of "Desensitization and the experimental reduction of threat." *Journal of Abnormal Psychology*, 1969, *74*, 86–87.

Davison, G.C. Noncontiguous presence during treatment sessions of relaxation and imaginal aversive stimuli: A reply to Nawas, Mealiea, and Fishman. *Behavior Therapy*, 1971, *2*, 357–360.

Davison, G.C., & Wilson, G.T. Critique of "Desensitization: Social and cognitive factors underlying the effectiveness of Wolpe's Procedure." *Psychological Bulletin*, 1972, *78*, 28–31.

Edelman, R.I. Desensitization and physiological arousal. *Journal of Personality and Social Psychology*, 1971, *17*, 259–266.

Fedoravicius, A.S. Self-instructional and relaxation variables in the systematic desensitization treatment of speech anxiety. *Dissertation Abstracts International*, 1972, *32*, 7290–7291.

Folkins, C.H., Evans, K.I., Opton, E.M. Jr., & Lazarus, R.S. Reply to Davison's critique. *Journal of Abnormal Psychology*, 1969, *74*, 88–89.

Folkins, C.H., Lawson, K.D., Opton, E.M., & Lazarus, R.S. Desensitization and the experimental reduction of threat. *Journal of Abnormal Psychology*, 1968, *73*, 100–113.

Fuhrer, R.E. The effects of covert sensitization with relaxation induction, covert sensitization without relaxation induction, and attention-placebo on the reduction of cigarette smoking. *Dissertation Abstracts International*, 1972, *32*, 6644–6645.

Geer, J.H., & Katkin, E.S. Treatment of insomnia using a variant of systematic desensitization. *Journal of Abnormal Psychology*, 1966, *71*, 161–164.

Grim, P.F. Relaxation therapies and neurosis: A central fatigue interpretation. *Psychosomatics*, 1972, *13*, 363–370.

Grings, W.W., & Uno, T. Counterconditioning: Fear and relaxation. *Psychophysiology*, 1968, *4*, 479–485.

Hampton, P.T. Systematic desensitization, flooding, and relaxation training as treatments for test anxiety. *Dissertation Abstracts International*, 1972, *32*, 5441.

Ince, L.P. Length of time required for relaxation in behavior therapy: A comparison of therapist and patient as relaxing agents. *Proceedings of the Annual Convention of the American Psychological Association*, 1970, *5*, 519–520.

Jacobs, A., & Wolpin, M. A second look at systematic desensitization. In A. Jacobs & L.B. Sachs (Eds.), *The Psychology of Private Events*. New York: Academic Press, 1971, pp. 77–108.

Johnson, S.M., & Sechrest, L. Comparison of desensitization and progressive relaxation in treating test anxiety. *Journal of Consulting & Clinical Phychology*, 1968, *32*, 280–286.

Kondas, O. Reduction of examination anxiety and 'stage-fright' by group desensitization and relaxation. *Behaviour Research & Therapy*, 1967, *5*, 275–281.

Lang, P.J., Lazovik, A.D., & Reynolds, D.J. Desensitization, suggestibility, and pseudotherapy. *Journal of Abnormal Psychology*, 1965, *70*, 395–402.

Laxer, R.M., Quarter, J., Kooman, A., & Walker, K. Systematic desensitization and relaxation of high-test-anxious secondary school students. *Journal of Counseling Psychology*, 1969, *16*, 446–451.

Laxer, R.M., & Walker, K. Counterconditioning versus relaxation in the desensitization of test anxiety. *Journal of Counseling Psychology*, 1970, *17*, 431–436.

Lehrer, P.M. Physiological effects of relaxation in a double-blind analog of desensitization. *Behavior Therapy*, 1972, *3*, 193–208.

Lomont, J.F., & Edwards, J.E. The role of relaxation in systematic desensitization. *Behaviour Research & Therapy*, 1967, *5*, 11–25.

Marshall, W.L., Strawbridge, H., & Keltner, A. The role of mental relaxation in experimental desensitization. *Behaviour Research and Therapy*, 1972, *10*, 355–366.

Mathews, A.M. Psychophysiological approaches to the investigation of desensitization and related procedures. *Psychological Bulletin*, 1971, *76*, 73–91.

McReynolds, W.T. A note on relaxation treatment groups in studies of systematic desensitization. *Journal of Abnormal Psychology*, 1969, *74*, 561–562.

McReynolds, W.T., & Tori, C. A further assessment of attention-placebo effects and demand characteristics in studies of systematic desensitization. *Journal of Consulting and Clinical Psychology*, 1972, *38*, 261–264.

Melville, C.H. Systematic desensitization: The roles of muscular relaxation and positive mental imagery. *Dissertation Abstracts International*, 1972, *32*, 4864.

Nawas, N.M., Welsch, W.V., & Fishman, S.T. The comparative effectiveness of pairing aversive imagery with relaxation, neutral tasks, and muscular tension in reducing snake phobia. *Behaviour Research & Therapy*, 1970, *8*, 63–68.

Persely, G., & Leventhal, D.B. The effects of therapeutically oriented instructions and of the pairing of anxiety imagery and relaxation in systematic desensitization. *Behavior Therapy*, 1972, *3*, 417–424.

Pilgrim, D.L. A comparison of behavior therapy techniques in the experimental reduction of psychophysiological stress. *Dissertation Abstracts International*, 1972, *32*, 5455.

Rachman, S. Studies in desensitization I: The separate effects of relaxation and desensitization. *Behaviour Research & Therapy*, 1965, *3*, 245–252.

Rachman, S. Systematic desensitization. *Psychological Bulletin*, 1967, *67*, 93–103.

Rachman, S. The role of muscular relaxation in desensitization therapy. *Behaviour Research & Therapy*, 1968, *6*, 159–166.

Rugel, R.P. Systematic desensitization of snake fear under two expectancy conditions and two relaxation conditions. *Dissertation Abstracts International*, 1972, *32*, 5458.

Sloan, J.L. The role of muscular relaxation and muscular tension as competing responses in the systematic desensitization of snake phobia. *Dissertation Abstracts International*, 1972, *32*, 6663.

Sue, D. The hole of relaxation in systematic desensitization. *Behaviour Research & Therapy*, 1972, *10*, 153–158.

Tanner, B.A. A case report on the use of relaxation and systematic desensitization to control multiple compulsive behaviors. *Journal of Behavior Therapy and Experimental Psychiatry*, 1971, *2*, 267–272.

Tasto, D.L. Systematic desensitization, muscle relaxation and visual imagery in the counterconditioning of four-year-old phobic child. *Behaviour Research & Therapy*, 1969, *7*, 409–411.

Van Egeren, L.F. Psychophysiological aspects of systematic desensitization: Some outstanding issues. *Behaviour Research and Therapy*, 1971, *9*, 65–77.

Waters, W.F., McDonald, D.G., & Koresko, R.L. Psychophysiological responses during analogue systematic desensitization and non-relaxation control procedures. *Behaviour Research and Therapy*, 1972, *10*, 381–393.

Wilkins, W. Desensitization: Social and cognitive factors underlying the effectiveness of Wolpe's procedure. *Psychological Bulletin*, 1971, *76*, 311–317.

Wilkins, W. Desensitization: Getting it together with Davison and Wilson. *Psychological Bulletin*, 1972, *78*, 32–36.

Wolpe, J. *Psychotherapy by Reciprocal Inhibition*. Stanford: Stanford University Press, 1958.

Zeisset, R.M. Desensitization and relaxation in the modification of psychiatric patients' interview behavior. *Journal of Abnormal Psychology*, 1968, *73*, 18–24.

III. Relaxation and Biofeedback

Beatty, J. Effects of initial alpha wave abundance and operant training procedures on occipital alpha and beta wave activity. *Psychonomic Science,* 1971, *23,* 197–199.

Beatty, J. Similar effects of feedback signals and instructional information on EEG activity. *Physiology and Behavior,* 1972, *9,* 151–154.

Blanchard, E.B., & Young, L.D. Self-control of cardiac functioning: A promise as yet unfulfilled. *Psychological Bulletin,* 1973, *79,* 145–163.

Brown, B.B. Recognition of aspects of consciousness through association with EEG alpha activity represented by a light signal. *Psychophysiology,* 1970, *6,* 442–452.

Brown, B.B. Awareness of EEG-subjective activity relationships detected within a closed feedback system. *Psychophysiology,* 1971, *7,* 451–464.

Budzynski, T.H., & Stoyva, J.M. An instrument for producing deep muscle relaxation by means of analog information feedback. *Journal of Applied Behavior Analysis,* 1969, *2,* 231–237.

Budzynski, T.H., Stoyva, J.M., & Adler, C. Feedback-induced muscle relaxation: Application to tension headache. *Journal of Behavior Therapy and Experimental Psychiatry,* 1970, *1,* 205–211.

Budzynski, T.H., & Stoyva, J.M. A biofeedback technique for teaching voluntary relaxation of the masseter. *Journal of Dental Research,* 1973, *52,* 116–119.

Budzynski, T.H., & Stoyva, J.M. EMG biofeedback in behavior therapy. In R. Jurjevich (Ed.), *Direct Psychotherapy: Developments on Four Continents.* Coral Gables, Florida: University of Miami Press, in press.

Budzynski, T.H., Stoyva, J.M., Adler, C.S., & Mullaney, D.J. EMG biofeedback and tension headache: A controlled outcome study. *Psychosomatic Medicine,* 1973, *35,* 484–496.

Caronite, S.C. The effects of biofeedback variables on the acquisition and retention of a differentiated electromyographic response. *Dissertation Abstracts International,* 1972, *33,* 1812.

Davidson, R.J., & Krippner, S. Biofeedback research: The data and their implications. In J. Stoyva, T.X. Barber, L.V. DiCara, J. Kamiya, N.E. Miller, & D. Shapiro (Eds.), *Bio-*

feedback and Self Control: 1971. Chicago: Aldine, 1972, pp. 3–34.

Davis, M.H. Relaxation training, facilitated by biofeedback apparatus, as a supplemental treatment in bronchial asthma. *Dissertation Abstracts International,* 1972, *33,* 1786.

Davis, M.H., Saunders, D., Creer, T., & Chai, H. Relaxation training facilitated by biofeedback apparatus as a supplemental treatment in bronchial asthma *Journal of Psychosomatic Research,* 1973, *17,* 121–128.

Engel, R.R. Measurement and quantification of surface EMG signals in states of relaxation. In D. Shapiro, T.X. Barber, L.V. DiCara, J. Kamiya, N.E. Miller, & J. Stoyva (Eds.), *Biofeedback and Self-Control: 1972.* Chicago: Aldine, 1973, pp. 508–509. (Abstract).

Gaarder, K. Control of states of consciousness: II. Attainment through external feedback augmenting control of psychophysiological variables. *Archives of General Psychiatry,* 1971, *25,* 436–441.

Green, E.E. Green, A.M., & Walters, D.E. Voluntary control of internal states: Psychological and physiological. *Journal of Transpersonal Psychology,* 1970, *2,* 1–26.

Green, E.E., Walters, D.E., Green, A.M., & Murphy, G. Feedback technique for deep relaxation. *Psychophysiology,* 1969, *6,* 371–377.

Green, E. Biofeedback for mind-body self-regulation: Healing and creativity. In D. Shapiro, T.X. Barber, L.V. DiCara, J. Kamiya, N.E. Miller, & J. Stoyva (Eds.), *Biofeedback and Self-Control: 1972.* Chicago: Aldine, 1973, pp. 152–166.

Grim, P. Anxiety change produced by self-induced muscle tension and by relaxation with respiration feedback. *Behavior Therapy,* 1971, *2,* 11–17.

Harrison, A., & Connolly, K. The conscious control of fine levels of neuro-muscular firing in spastic and normal subjects. *Developmental Medicine and Child Neurology,* 1971, *13,* 762–771.

Hart, J.T. Autocontrol of EEG alpha. *Psychophysiology,* 1968, *4,* 506 (Abstract).

Hefferline, R.F., & Bruno, L.J.J. The psychophysiology of private events. In A. Jacobs & L.B. Sachs (Eds.), *The Psychology of Private Events.* New York: Academic Press, 1971, pp. 163–192.

Honorton, C., Davidson, R., & Bindler, P. Shifts in subjective state associated with feedback-augmented EEG alpha. *Psychophysiology,* 1972, *9,* 269–270 (Abstract).

Hord, D., & Barber, J. Alpha control: Effectiveness of two kinds of feedback. *Psychonomic Science,* 1971, *25,* 151–154.

Hord, D., Naitoh, P., & Johnson, L.C. EEG spectral features

of self-regulated high alpha states. *Psychophysiology,* 1972, *9,* 278 (Abstract).

Jacobs, A., & Felton, G.S. Visual feedback of myoelectric output to facilitate muscle relaxation in normal persons and patients with neck injuries. *Archives of Physical Medicine and Rehabilitation,* 1969, *50,* 34–39.

Kamiya, J. Operant control of the EEG alpha rhythm and some of its reported effects on consciousness. In C.T. Tart (Ed.), *Altered States of Consciousness.* New York: Wiley & Sons, 1969, pp. 507–517.

Kiefer, D. EEG alpha feedback and subjective states of consciousness. *Psychologia,* 1971, *14,* 3–14.

Leaf, W.B., & Gaarder, K.R. A simplified electromyograph feedback apparatus for relaxation training. *Journal of Behavior Therapy and Experimental Psychiatry,* 1971, *2,* 39–43.

Lynch, J.J., & Paskewitz, D.A. On the mechanisms of the feedback control of human brain wave activity. *Journal of Nervous and Mental Disease,* 1971, *153,* 205–217.

Matus, I. Internal awareness, muscle sense and muscle relaxation in bioelectric information feedback-training. *Dissertation Abstracts International,* 1972, *33,* 1309.

McGuigan, F.J. External auditory feedback from covert oral behavior during silent reading. *Psychonomic Science,* 1971, *25,* 212–214.

Mulholland, T.B. Occipital alpha revisited. *Psychological Bulletin,* 1972, *78,* 176–182.

Murphy, G. Experiments in overcoming self-deception. *Psychophysiology,* 1970, *6,* 790–799.

Nideffer, R.M. Alpha and the development of human potential. In D. Shapiro, T.X. Barber, L.V. DiCara, J. Kamiya, N.E. Miller, & J. Stoyva (Eds.), *Biofeedback and Self-Control: 1972.* Chicago: Aldine, 1973, pp. 167–188.

Nowlis, D.P., & Kamiya, J. The control of electroencephalographic alpha rhythms through auditory feedback and the associated mental activity. *Psychophysiology,* 1970, *6,* 476–484.

Paskewitz, D.A., Lynch, J.J., Orne, M.F., & Costello, J. The feedback control of alpha activity: Conditioning or disinhibition. *Psychophysiology,* 1970, *6,* 637–638 (Abstract).

Paskewitz, D.A., & Orne, M.T. Visual effects on alpha feedback training. *Science,* 1973, *181,* 360–363.

Peper, E. Feedback regulation of the alpha electroencephalogram activity through control of the internal and external parameters. *Kybernetik,* 1970, *7,* 107–112.

Peper, E. Developing a biofeedback model: Alpha EEG feedback as a means for pain control. Paper presented at the Biofeedback Research Society, St. Louis, 1971.

Peper, E. Reduction of efferent motor commands during alpha feedback as a facilitator of EEG Alpha and a precondition for changes in consciousness. *Kybernetik*, 1971, *9*, 226–231.

Peper, E. Localized EEG alpha feedback training: A possible technique for mapping subjective, conscious and behavioral experiences. *Kybernetik*, 1972, *11*, 166–169.

Peper, E., & Mulholland, T. Methodological and theoretical problems in the voluntary control of electroencephalographic occipital alpha by the subject. *Kybernetik*, 1970, *7*, 10–13.

Quinton, E.E. Biofeedback indicators of tension-relaxation. *Proceedings of the Annual Convention of the American Psychological Association*, 1972, *7*, 999.

Raskin, M., Johnson, G., & Rondestvedt, J. Chronic anxiety treated by feedback-induced muscle relaxation. *Archives of General Psychiatry*, 1973, *28*, 263–267.

Regestein, Q.R., Pegram, G.V., Cook, B., & Bradley, D. Alpha rhythm percentage maintained during 4- and 12-hour feedback periods. *Psychosomatic Medicine*, 1973, *35*, 215–222.

Riddick, J.C. The efficacy of automated relaxation training with response contingent feedback. *Dissertation Abstracts International*, 1972, *32*, 4869.

Schmeidler, G., & Lewis, L. Mood changes after alpha feedback training. *Perceptual & Motor Skills*, 1971, *32*, 709–710.

Schwartz, G.E., Shaw, G., & Shapiro, D. Specificity of alpha and heart rate control through feedback. *Psychophysiology*, 1972, *9*, 269 (Abstract).

Sittenfeld, P. The control of the EEG theta rhythm. In D. Shapiro, T.X. Barber, L.V. DiCara, J. Kamiya, N.E. Miller, & J. Stoyva (Eds.), *Biofeedback and Self-Control: 1972*. Chicago: Aldine, 1973, pp. 506–507.

Stoyva, J. Biofeedback techniques and the conditions for hallucinatory activity. In F.J. McGuigan and R.A. Schoonover (Eds.), *The Psychophysiology of Thinking*. New York: Academic Press, 1973, pp. 387–414.

Stoyva, J., & Budzynski, T.H. Cultivated low arousal—an anti-stress response. In L.V. DiCara (Ed.), *Limbic and Autonomic Nervous System Research*, New York: Plenum Press, 1974.

Travis, T.A., Kondo, C.Y., & Knott, J. R. A controlled study of alpha enhancement *Psychophysiology*, 1972, *9*, 268–269 (Abstract).

Walsch, D.H. Social, cognitive and electroencephalographic effects in alpha feedback training. *Dissertation Abstracts International*, 1972, *33*, 1775.

Wickramasekera, I. Instructions and EMG feedback in systematic desensitization: A case report. *Behavior Therapy*, 1972, *3*, 460–465.

Wickramasekera, I. Electromyographic feedback training and tension headache: Preliminary observations. *American Journal of Clinical Hypnosis*, 1972, *15*, 83–85.

Woodruff, D.S. Biofeedback control of the EEG alpha rhythm and its effect on reaction time in the young and old. *Dissertation Abstracts International*, 1972, *33*, 1833–1834.

IV. Relaxation and Hypnotic Suggestion

Barber, T.X., & Calverley, D.S. Empirical evidence for a theory of "hypnotic" behavior: The suggestibility-enhancing effects of motivational suggestions, relaxation-sleep suggestions, and suggestions that the S will be effectively "hypnotized." *Journal of Personality*, 1965, *33*, 256–270.

Barber, T.X., & Hahn, K.W. Hypnotic induction and "relaxation": An experimental study. *Archives of General Psychiatry*, 1963, *33*, 295–300.

Ham, M.W., & Edmonston, W.E., Jr. Hypnosis, relaxation and motor retardation. *Journal of Abnormal Psychology*, 1971, *77*, 329–331.

McAmmond, D.M., Davidson, P.O., & Kovitz, D.M. A comparison of the effects of hypnosis and relaxation training on stress reactions in a dental situation. *American Journal of Clinical Hypnosis*, 1971, *13*, 233–242.

Paul, G.L. Physiological effects of relaxation training and hypnotic suggestion. *Journal of Abnormal Psychology*, 1969, *74*, 425–437.

Paul, G.L. Extraversion, emotionality, and physiological response to relaxation training and hypnotic suggestion. *International Journal of Clinical & Experimental Hypnosis*, 1969, *17*, 89–98.

Paul, G.L. Inhibition of physiological response to stressful imagery by relaxation training and hypnotically suggested relaxation. *Behaviour Research & Therapy*, 1969, 7, 249–256.

Paul, G.L., & Trimble, R.W. Recorded vs. "live" relaxation training and hypnotic suggestion: Comparative effectiveness for reducing physiological arousal and inhibiting stress response. *Behavior Therapy*, 1970, *1*, 285–302.

Sachs, L.B. Comparison of hypnotic analgesia and hypnotic relaxation during stimulation by a continuous pain source. *Journal of Abnormal Psychology*, 1970, *76*, 206–210.

Sherman, S.E. Very deep hypnosis: An experiential and electroencephalographic investigation. *Dissertation Abstracts International*, 1972, *32*, 6039–6040.

Sherman, S.E. Brief report: Continuing research on "very deep hypnosis." *Journal of Transpersonal Psychology*, 1972, *4*, 87–91.

Tart, C.T. Transpersonal potentialities of deep hypnosis. *Journal of Transpersonal Psychology*, 1970, *2*, 27–40.

V. Relaxation and Hypnotic Susceptibility

Akpinar, S., Ulett, G.A., & Itil, T.M. Hypnotizability predicted by digital computer-analyzed EEG pattern. *Biological Psychiatry*, 1971, *3*, 387–392.

Engstrom, D.R., London, P., & Hart, J.T. Hypnotic susceptibility increased by EEG alpha training. *Nature*, 1970, *227*, 1261–1262.

Engstrom, D.R. Interactional effects of muscle tension and EEG alpha production on hypnotic susceptibility. *Proceedings of the Annual Convention of the American Psychological Association*, 1972, *7*, 1012.

Engstrom, D.R., London, P., & Hart, J.T. EEG alpha feedback training and hypnotic susceptibility. *Proceedings of the Annual Convention of the American Psychological Association*, 1970, *5*, 837–838.

Galbraith, G.C., London, P., Leibovitz, M.P., Cooper, L.M., & Hart, J.T. EEG and hypnotic susceptibility. *Journal of Comparative and Physiological Psychology*, 1970, *72*, 125–131.

London, P., Hart, J.T., & Leibovitz, M.P. EEG alpha rhythms and susceptibility to hypnosis. *Nature*, 1968, *219*, 71–72.

Nowlis, D.P., & Rhead, J.C. Relation of eyes-closed resting EEG alpha activity to hypnotic susceptibility. *Perceptual & Motor Skills*, 1968, *27*, 1047–1050.

Ulett, G.A., Akpinar, S., & Itil, T.M. Hypnosis: Physiological and pharmacological reality. *American Journal of Psychiatry*, 1972, *128*, 799–805.

Wickramasekera, I. Effects of EMG feedback training on susceptibility to hypnosis: Preliminary observation. *Proceedings of the Annual Convention of the American Psychological Association*, 1971, *6*, 783–784.

Wickramasekera, I. Effects of EMG feedback training on hypnotic susceptibility: more preliminary observations. *Proceedings of the 80th Annual Convention of the American Psychological Association*, 1972, *7*, 1012.

VI. Relaxation and Sleep Onset

Bertini, M., Lewis, H.B., & Witkin, H.A. Some preliminary observations with an experimental procedure for the study of hynagogic and related phenomena. In C.T. Tart (Ed.), *Altered States of Consciousness*. New York: Wiley, 1969. pp. 93–111.

Budzynski, T.H. Some applications of biofeedback-produced twilight states. *Fields within fields . . . within fields*, 1972, 5, 105–114.

Foulkes, D. Theories of dream formation and recent studies of sleep consciousness. *Psychological Bulletin*, 1964, 62, 236–247.

Foulkes, D. *The Psychology of Sleep*. New York: Scribners, 1966.

Foulkes, D., Spear, P., & Symonds, J. Individual differences in mental activity at sleep onset. *Journal of Abnormal Psychology*, 1966, 71, 280–286.

Foulkes, D., & Vogel, G. Mental activity at sleep onset. *Journal of Abnormal Psychology*, 1965, 70, 231–243.

Gastaut, H. Hypnosis and pre-sleep patterns. In L. Chertok (Ed.), *Psychophysiological Mechanisms of Hypnosis*. New York: Springer-Verlag, 1969, pp. 40–44.

Goodenough, D., Lewis, H., Shapiro, A., Jaret, L., & Sleser, I. Dream reporting following abrupt and gradual awakening from different types of sleep. *Journal of Personality and Social Psychology*, 1965, 2, 170–179.

Hauri, P. Evening activity, sleep mentation, and subjective sleep quality. *Journal of Abnormal Psychology*, 1970, 76, 270–275.

Hollingworth, H. The psychology of drowsiness: An introspective and analytic study. *American Journal of Psychology*, 1911, 22, 99–111.

Isakower, D. A contribution to the psychopathology of phenomena associated with falling asleep. *International Journal of Psychoanalysis*, 1938, 19, 331–345.

Jacobson, E. *You can sleep well: The ABC's of restful sleep for the average person*. New York: McGraw Hill, 1938.

Liberson, W., & Liberson, C. EEG records, reaction times, eye movements, respiration, and mental content during drowsiness. In J. Wortis (Ed.), *Recent advances in biological psychiatry*. New York: Plenum Press, 1966, 3, 295–302.

Luce, G.G., & Segal, J. *Insomnia: The guide for troubled sleepers.* Garden City: Doubleday, 1969.

McKeller, P., & Simpson, L. Between wakefulness and sleep. *British Journal of Psychology,* 1954, *45,* 266–276.

Monroe, L.J. Psychological and physiological differences between good and poor sleepers. *Journal of Abnormal Psychology,* 1967, *72,* 255–264.

Rappaport, D. States of consciousness: A psychopathological and psychodynamic view. In M.M. Gill (Ed.), *The collected papers of David Rappaport.* New York: Basic Books, 1967, pp. 385–404.

Singer, J.L. *Daydreaming: An introduction to the experimental study of inner experience.* New York: Random House, 1966.

Storms, M.D., & Nisbett, R.E. Insomnia and the attribution process. *Journal of Personality and Social Psychology,* 1970, *16,* 319–328.

Tart, C.T. Between waking and sleeping: the hypnagogic state. In C.T. Tart (Ed.), *Altered States of Consciousness.* New York: Wiley, 1969. pp. 73–74.

Varendonck, J. The psychology of daydreams. In D. Rappaport (Ed.), *Organization and Pathology of Thought.* New York: Columbia University Press, 1951, pp. 451–473.

Vogel, G., Foulkes, D., & Trosman, H. Ego functions and dreaming during sleep onset. *Archives of General Psychiatry,* 1966, *14,* 238–248.

Zuckerman, M., & Hopkins, T. Hallucination or dreams? A study of arousal levels and reported visual sensations during sensory deprivation. *Perceptual and Motor Skills,* 1966, *22,* 447–459.

VII. Autogenic Training

Geissmann, P., & Noel, C. EEG study with frequency analysis and polygraphy of autogenic training. *Proceedings of the 3rd World Congress of Psychiatry*, 1961, *3*, 468–472.

Gorton, B.E. Autogenic training. *American Journal of Clinical Hypnosis*, 1959, *2*, 31–41.

Jus, A., & Jus, K. Some remarks on "passive" concentration and on autogenic shift. In L. Chertok (Ed.), *Psychophysiological Mechanisms and Hypnosis*. Berlin: Springer-Verlag, 1969, pp. 52–57.

Langen, D. Peripheral changes in blood circulation during autogenic training and hypnosis (Results of experimental research). In L. Chertok (Ed.), *Psychophysiological Mechanisms of Hypnosis*. Berlin: Springer-Verlag, 1969, pp. 58–66.

Luthe, W. Method, research and application of autogenic training. *American Journal of Clinical Hypnosis*, 1962, *5*, 17–23.

Luthe, W. Autogenic training: Method, research and application in medicine. *American Journal of Psychotherapy*, 1963, *17*, 174–195.

Luthe, W. (Ed.) *Autogenic Therapy: Volumes I–VI*. New York: Grune & Stratton, 1969.

Luthe, W. Autogenic therapy: Excerpts on applications to cardiovascular disorders and hypercholesteremia. In J. Stoyva, T.X. Barber, L.V. DiCara, J. Kamiya, N.E. Miller, & D. Shapiro (Eds.), *Biofeedback and Self Control, 1971*. Chicago: Aldine, 1972, pp. 437–462.

Luthe, W., Jus, A., & Geissmann, P. Autogenic state and autogenic shift: Psychophysiologic and neurophysiologic aspects. *Acta Psychotherapeutica*, 1963, *11*, 1–13.

Meyer, R.G. Autogenic training: comparisons with progressive relaxation and systematic desensitization therapy. *Proceedings of the Annual Convention of the American Psychological Association*, 1972, 7, 999.

Reed, R. Utility of autogenic training with specific biofeedback indicators. *Proceedings of the Annual Convention of the American Psychological Association*, 1972, 7, 999.

Sargent, J.D., Green, E.E., & Walters, E.D. Preliminary report on the use of autogenic feedback training in the treatment of migraine and tension headaches. *Psychosomatic Medicine*, 1973, *35*, 129–135.

Schultz, J.H., & Luthe, W. *Autogenic training: A psychophysi-*

ologic approach to psychotherapy. New York: Grune &
Stratton, 1959.

Shibata, J.I. Limits of application of autogenic training to
schizophrenia and selection of the patients. *American Journal
of Clinical Hypnosis,* 1968, *11,* 99–100.

Shibata, J.I., & Kuwahara, M. Electroencephalographic studies
of schizophrenic patients treated with autogenic training.
American Journal of Clinical Hypnosis, 1967, *10,* 25–29.

Shibata, J.I., & Motoda, K. The application of autogenic training to a group of schizophrenic patients. *American Journal
of Clinical Hypnosis,* 1967, *10,* 15–19.

Shibata, J.I., & Motoda, K. Clinical evaluation with psychological tests of schizophrenic patients treated with autogenic
training. *American Journal of Clinical Hypnosis,* 1967, *10,*
20–24.

Snider, J.G., & Oetting, E.R. Autogenic training and the treatment of examination anxiety in students. *Journal of Clinical
Psychology,* 1966, *22,* 111–114.

Spoerri, Th. Autogenic training and psychosomatic disorders.
Psychotherapy & Psychosomatics, 1969, *17,* 354–364.

VIII. Meditation and Yoga

Akishige, Y. (Ed.) *Psychological Studies on Zen*. Tokyo, Japan: Zen Institute of Komazawa University, 1970.

Allison, J. Respiratory changes during the practice of the technique of Transcendental Meditation. *Lancet*, 1970, *7651*, 833–834.

Bagchi, B., & Wenger, M. Electrophysiological correlates of some yogi exercises. *Electroencephalography and Clinical Neurophysiology*, 1957, Suppl. 7, 132–149.

Banquet, J.P. EEG and meditation. *Electroencephalography & Clinical Neurophysiology*, 1972, *33*, 449–455.

Banquet, J.P. Spectral analysis of the EEG in meditation. *Electroencephalography & Clinical Neurophysiology*, 1973, *35*, 143–157.

Benson, H. Yoga for drug abuse. *New England Journal of Medicine*, 1969, *281*, 1133.

Boudreau, L. Transcendental meditation and yoga as reciprocal inhibitors. *Journal of Behavior Therapy and Experimental Psychiatry*, 1972, *3*, 97–98.

Dalal, A.S., & Barber, T.X. Yoga, "Yogic feats," and hypnosis in the light of empirical research. *American Journal of Clinical Hypnosis*, 1969, *11*, 155–166.

Das, J.P. Yoga and hypnosis. *International Journal of Clinical and Experimental Hypnosis*, 1963, *11*, 31-37.

Datey, K., Deshmukh, S., Dalvi, C., & Vinekar, S. "Shavasan": A yogic exercise in the management of hypertension. *Angiology*, 1969, *20*, 325–333.

Davidson, R.J., & Goleman, D.J. Attentional and affective concomitants of meditation: A cross-sectional study. *Journal of Abnormal Psychology*, in press.

Deikman, A.J. Experimental meditation. *Journal of Nervous and Mental Disease*, 1963, *136*, 329–343.

Deikman, A.J. Deautomatization and the mystic experience. *Psychiatry*, 1966, *29*, 324–338.

Deikman, A.J. Implications of experimentally induced contemplative meditation. *Journal of Nervous and Mental Disease*, 1966, *142*, 101–116.

Fisher, R. A cartography of ecstatic and meditative states. *Science*, 1971, *174*, 897–904.

Frederick, A.N., & Barber, T.X. Yoga, hypnosis and self-control of cardiovascular functions. *Proceedings of the Annual Convention of the American Psychological Association*, 1972, *7*, 859–860.

Fujisawa, K., Koga, E., & Toyoda, G. The polygraphical study on the psychogenic changes of consciousness [1]. About Zen, yoga, and hypnosis. *Electroencephalography and Clinical Neurophysiology*, 1959, Suppl. 18, 51.

Gellhorn, E., & Kiely, W.F. Mystical states of consciousness: Neurophysiological and clinical aspects. *Journal of Nervous & Mental Disease*, 1972, *154*, 399–405.

Gilbert, A. From Buddha to Pavlov—the technique of mysticism. *Psychologia*, 1967, *10*, 121–128.

Goleman, D. Meditation as meta-therapy: Hypotheses toward a proposed fifth state of consciousness. *Journal of Transpersonal Psychology*, 1971, *3*, 1-25.

Goleman, D. The Buddha on meditation and states of consciousness, Part I: The teachings. *Journal of Transpersonal Psychology*, 1972, *4*, 1–44.

Goleman, D. The Buddha on meditation and states of consciousness, Part II: A typology of meditation techniques. *Journal of Transpersonal Psychology*, 1972, *4*, 151–210.

Hirai, T. Electroencephalographic study on the Zen meditation (Zazen)—EEG changes during the concentrated relaxation. *Psychiatria et Neurologia Japonica*, 1960, *62*, 76–105.

Hirai, T., Izawa, S., & Koga, E. EEG and Zen Buddhism. EEG changes in the course of meditation. *Electroencephalography and Clinical Neurophysiology*, 1959, Suppl. 18, 52–53.

Kasamatsu, A., et al. The EEG of Zen and yoga practitioners. *Electroencephalography and Clinical Neurophysiology*, 1957, Suppl. 9, 51–52.

Kasamatsu, A., & Hirai, T. Science of Zazen. *Psychologia*, 1963, *6*, 86-91.

Kasamatsu, A., & Hirai, T. An electroencephalographic study on the Zen meditation (Zazen). *Psychologia*, 1969, *12*, 205–225.

Kasamatsu, A., Hirai, T., & Ando, N. EEG responses to click stimulation in Zen meditation. *Proceedings of the Japanese EEG Society*, 1962, 77–78.

Kretschmer, W. Meditative techniques in psychotherapy. *Psychologia*, 1962, *5*, 76-83.

Lesh, T.V. Zen meditation and the development of empathy in counselors. *Journal of Humanistic Psychology*, 1970, *10*, 39–74.

Leung, P. Comparative effects of training in external and internal concentration on two counseling behaviors. *Journal of Counseling Psychology*, 1973, *20*, 227–234.

Levander, V., Benson, H., Wheeler, R., & Wallace, R.K. Increased forearm blood flow during a wakeful hypometabolic state. *Federal Proceedings*, 1972, *31*, 405.

Maupin, E.W. Zen Buddhism: A psychological review. *Journal of Consulting Psychology*, 1962, *26*, 362–378.

Maupin, E.W. Individual differences in response to a Zen meditation exercise. *Journal of Consulting Psychology*, 1965, *29*, 139–145.

Maupin, E.W. On meditation. In C.T. Tart (Ed.), *Altered States of Consciousness*. New York: Wiley, 1969, pp. 177–186.

Miles, W. Oxygen consumption during three yoga-type breathing patterns. *Journal of Applied Physiology*, 1964, *19*, 75–82.

Naranjo, C., & Ornstein, R.E. *On the Psychology of Meditation.* New York: The Viking Press, 1971.

Nidich, S., Seeman, W., & Dreskin, T. Influence of Transcendental Meditation: A replication. *Journal of Counseling Psychology*, in press.

Nidich, S., Seeman, W., & Siebert, M. Influence of Transcendental Meditation on state anxiety. *Journal of Consulting and Clinical Psychology*, in press.

Orme-Johnson, D.W. Autonomic stability and Transcendental Meditation. *Psychosomatic Medicine*, 1973, *35*, 341–349.

Ramamurthi, B. Yoga—an explanation and probable neurophysiology. *Journal of the Indian Medical Association*, 1967, *48*, 167–170.

Rao, L. Yoga and autohypnotism. *British Journal of Medical Hypnotism*, 1965, *17*, 38–40.

Seeman, W., Nidich, S., & Banta, T. Influence of Transcendental Meditation on a measure of self-actualization. *Journal of Counseling Psychology*, 1972, *19*, 184–187.

Tart, C.T. A psychologist's experience with Transcendental Meditation. *Journal of Transpersonal Psychology*, 1972, *3*, 135–140.

Timmons, B., & Kamiya, J. The psychology and physiology of meditation and related phenomena: A bibliography. *Journal of Transpersonal Psychology*, 1970, *2*, 41–59.

Udupa, K.N. The scientific basis of yoga. *Journal of the American Medical Association*, 1972, *220*, 1365.

Van Nuys, D. A novel technique for studying attention during meditation. *Journal of Transpersonal Psychology*, 1971, *2*, 125–133.

Van Nuys, D. Meditation, attention, and hypnotic susceptibility: A correlational study. *International Journal of Clinical and Experimental Hypnosis*, 1973, *21*, 59–69.

Wallace, R.K. Physiological effects of Transcendental Meditation. *Science*, 1970, *167*, 1751–1754.

Wallace, R.K. & Benson, H. The physiology of meditation. *Scientific American*, 1972, *226*, 84–90.

Wallace, R.K., Benson, H., & Wilson, A.F. A wakeful hypometabolic physiologic state. *American Journal of Physiology*, 1971, *221*, 795–799.

Wallace, R.K., Benson, H., Wilson, A.F. & Garrett, M.D. Decreased blood lactate during Transcendental Meditation.
Federal Proceedings, 1971, *30,* 376.

Watanabe, T., Shapiro, D., & Schwartz, G.E. Meditation as an
anoxic state: A critical review and theory. *Psychophysiology,*
1972, *9,* 279 (Abstract).

Wilson, A.F., & Honsberger, R. The effects of Transcendental
Meditation upon bronchial asthma. *Clinical Research,* in
press.

IX. Relaxation and Paranormal Processes

Braud, W.G., & Braud, L.W. Preliminary explorations of Psi-conducive states: Progressive muscular relaxation. *Journal of the American Society for Psychical Research*, 1973, *67*, 26–46.

Cadoret, R.J. An exploratory experiment: Continuous EEG recording during clairvoyant card tests. *Journal of Parapsychology*, 1964, *28*, 226. (Abstract).

Chari, C.T.K. Psychophysiological issues about EEG alpha activity and ESP. *Journal of the American Society for Psychical Research*. 1970, *64*, 411–420.

Honorton, C., & Barksdale, W. PK performance with waking suggestions for muscle tension versus relaxation. *Journal of the American Society for Psychical Research*, 1972, *66*, 208–214.

Honorton, C. & Carbone, M. A preliminary study of feedback-augmented EEG alpha activity and ESP card-guessing performance. *Journal of the American Society for Psychical Research*, 1971, *65*, 66–74.

Honorton, C., Davidson, R., & Bindler, P. Feedback augmented EEG alpha, shifts in subjective state, and ESP card-guessing performance. *Journal of the American Society for Psychical Research*, 1971, *65*, 308–323.

Lewis, L., & Schmeidler, G.R. Analysis of alpha-ESP relations for ESP calls with feedback and for other responses made without knowledge that they would be scored for ESP. *Journal of Parapsychology*, 1970, *34*, 327–328. (Abstract).

Lewis, L., & Schmeidler, G.R. Alpha relations with non-intentional and purposeful ESP after feedback. *Journal of the American Society for Psychical Research*, 1971, *65*, 455–467.

Morris, R.L., & Cohen, D. A preliminary experiment on the relationships among ESP, alpha rhythm, and calling patterns. *Journal of Parapsychology*, 1969, *33*, 341 (Abstract).

Morris, R.L., Roll, W.G., Klein, J., & Wheeler, G. EEG patterns and ESP results in forced-choice experiments with Lalsingh Harribance. *Journal of the American Society for Psychical Research*, 1972, *66*, 253–268.

Osis, K., & Bokert, E. ESP and changed states of consciousness induced by meditation. *Journal of the American Society for Psychical Research*, 1971, *65*, 17–65.

Otani, S. Relations of mental set and change of skin resistance to ESP score. *Journal of Parapsychology,* 1955, *19,* 164–170.

Stanford, R.G. EEG alpha activity and ESP performance: A Replicative study. *Journal of the American Society for Psychical Research,* 1971, *65,* 144–154.

Stanford, R.G., & Lovin, C.A. EEG alpha activity and ESP performance. *Journal of the American Society for Psychical Research,* 1970, *64,* 375–384.

Stanford, R.G., & Stanford, B.E. Shifts in EEG alpha rhythms as related to calling patterns and ESP run-score variance. *Journal of Parapsychology,* 1969, *33,* 39–47.

Tart, C. T. A second psychophysiological study of out-of-the-body experiences in a gifted subject. *International Journal of Parapsychology,* 1967, *9,* 251–258.

Tart, C.T. A psychophysiological study of out-of-the-body experiences in a selected subject. *Journal of the American Society for Psychical Research,* 1968, 62, 3–27.

X. Clinical Applications of Relaxation and Related States

Alexander, A.B. Systematic relaxation and flow rates in asthmatic children: Relationship to emotional precipitants and anxiety. *Journal of Psychosomatic Research,* in press.

Alexander, A.B., Miklich, D.R., & Hershkoff, H. The immediate effects of systematic relaxation training on peak expiratory flow rates in asthmatic children. *Psychosomatic Medicine,* 1972, *34,* 388–394.

Bagchi, B. Mental hygiene and the Hindu doctrine of relaxation. *Mental Hygiene,* 1936, *20,* 424–440.

Baker, B.L., & Kahn, M. A reply to "Critique of 'Treatment of insomnia by relaxation training': Relaxation training, Rogerian therapy or demand characteristics." *Journal of Abnormal Psychology,* 1972, *79,* 94–96.

Braatoy, T. Psychology vs. anatomy in the treatment of "arm neuroses" with physiotherapy. *Journal of Nervous and Mental Disease,* 1952, *115,* 215–245.

Budzynski, T., & Stoyva, J. Biofeedback techniques in behavior therapy and autogenic training. Unpublished manuscript.

Davison, G.C. Differential relaxation and cognitive restructuring in therapy with a "paranoid schizophrenic" or "paranoid state." *Proceedings of the 74th Annual Convention of the American Psychological Association,* 1966, 177–178.

Eisenman, R. Critique of "Treatment of insomnia by relaxation training": Relaxation training, Rogerian therapy, or demand characteristics? *Journal of Abnormal Psychology,* 1970, *75,* 315–316.

Gannon, L., & Sternbach, R.A. Alpha enhancement as a treatment for pain: A case study. *Behavior Therapy & Experimental Psychiatry,* 1971, *2,* 209–213.

Glassford, P.V. Staff experimental relaxation group. *Australian Occupational Therapy Journal,* 1972, *19,* 51–54.

Graziano, A.M., & Kean, J.E. Programmed relaxation and reciprocal inhibition with psychotic children. *Behaviour Research & Therapy,* 1968, *6,* 433–437.

Grim, P.F. Psychotherapy by somatic alternation. *Mental Hygiene,* 1969, *53,* 451–458.

Gruen, W. A successful application of systematic self-relaxation and self-suggestions about postoperative reactions in a case of cardiac surgery. *International Journal of Clinical and Experimental Hypnosis,* 1972, *20,* 143–151.

Gurman, A.S. Treatment of a case of public-speaking anxiety *in vivo* by desensitization and cue controlled relaxation. *Journal of Behavior Therapy & Experimental Psychiatry*, 1973, *4*, 51–54.

Hart, J.T. Beyond psychotherapy—a programmatic essay on the applied psychology of the future. In J.T. Hart & T.M. Tomlinson (Eds.), *New Directions in Client-Centered Therapy.* New York: Houghton-Mufflin, 1970, pp. 563–595.

Hartman, C.H. Group relaxation training for control of impulsive behavior in alcoholics. *Behavior Therapy*, 1973, *4*, 173–174.

Howard, T.J. Cramping, relaxation and hemodialysis. *Dissertation Abstracts International*, 1972, *32*, 4860.

Jacobson, E. (Ed.) *Modern Treatment of Tense Patients.* Springfield, Ill.: C.C. Thomas, 1970.

Jones, F.P. Method for changing stereotyped response patterns by the inhibition of certain postural sets. *Psychological Review*, 1965, *72*, 196–214.

Kahn, M., Baker, B.L., & Weiss, J.M. Treatment of insomnia by relaxation training. *Journal of Abnormal Psychology*, 1968, *73*, 556–558.

Miller, P.M. The use of visual imagery and muscle relaxation in the counter-conditioning of a phobic child: A case study. *Journal of Nervous and Mental Disease*, 1972, *154*, 457–460.

Mitchell, K.R. A psychological approach to the treatment of migraine. *British Journal of Psychiatry*, 1971, *119*, 533–534.

Mitchell, K.R., & Mitchell, D.M. Migraine: An exploratory treatment application of programmed behavior therapy techniques. *Journal of Psychosomatic Research*, 1971, *15*, 137–157.

Nideffer, R.M., & Deckner, C.W. A case study of improved athletic performance following use of relaxation procedures. *Perceptual and Motor Skills*, 1970, *30*, 821–822.

O'Brien, J.S., Raynes, A.E., & Patch, V.D. Treatment of heroin addiction with aversion therapy, relaxation training and systematic desensitization. *Behaviour Research & Therapy*, 1972, *10*, 77–80.

Rathbone, J.L. *Relaxation.* Philadelphia: Lea & Febiger, 1969.

Russell, R.K., & Sipich, J.F. Cue controlled relaxation in the treatment of test anxiety. *Journal of Behavior Therapy and Experimental Psychiatry*, 1973, *4*, 47–49.

Shapiro, D., & Schwartz, G.E. Biofeedback and visceral learning: Clinical applications. *Seminars in Psychiatry*, 1972, *4*, 171–184.

Stone, W.O. A study of pre-recorded relaxation training, rational-emotive and personal-growth group counseling intervention techniques in the reduction of state anxiety in black multi-occupational trainees. *Dissertation Abstracts International*, 1972, *32*, 6772.

Suinn, R.M., & Brittain, J. The termination of an LSD "freak-out" through the use of relaxation. *Journal of Clinical Psychology*, 1970, *26*, 127–128.

Tophoff, M. Massed practice, relaxation and assertion training in the treatment of Gilles de la Tourette's syndrome. *Journal of Behavior Therapy and Experimental Psychiatry*, 1973, *4*, 71–73.

Webster, D.R. The inhibition of agitative-disruptive behaviors in retardates by an overcorrective relaxation procedure. *Dissertation Abstracts International*, 1972, *33*, 2361.

Webster, D.R., & Azrin, N.H. Required relaxation: A method of inhibitory agitative-disruptive behavior of retardates. *Behavior Research & Therapy*, 1973, *11*, 67–78.

Weinman, B., Gelbart, P., Wallace, M., & Post, M. Inducing assertive behavior in chronic schizophrenics: A comparison of socio-environmental, desensitization, and relaxation therapies. *Journal of Consulting and Clinical Psychology*, 1972, *39*, 246–252.

Whatmore, G., & Kohli, D.R. Dysponesis: A neuropsychologic factor in functional disorders. *Behavioral Science*, 1968, *13*, 102–124.

XI. Physiological and Theoretical Issues

Cabanac, M. Physiological role of pleasure. *Science*, 1971, *173*, 1103–1107.

Davison, G.C. Anxiety under total curarization: Implications for the role of muscular relaxation in the desensitization of neurotic fears. *Journal of Nervous & Mental Disease*, 1966, *143*, 443-448.

Davison, G.C., & Valins, S. On self-produced and drug-produced relaxation. *Behavior Research and Therapy*, 1968, *6*, 401–402.

Davison, G.C., & Valins, S. A reply to Wolpe's critique regarding self-produced and drug-produced relaxation. *Behavior Research & Therapy*, 1970, *8*, 107–108.

Deikman, A.J. Bimodal consciousness. *Archives of General Psychiatry*, 1971, *25*, 481–489.

Gellhorn, E. The physiological basis of neuromuscular relaxation. *Archives of Internal Medicine*, 1958, *102*, 392–399.

Gellhorn, E. Motion and emotion: The role of proprioception in the physiology and pathology of the emotions. *Psychological Review*, 1964, *71*, 457–472.

Hilgard, E.R. Altered states of awareness. *Journal of Nervous and Mental Disease*, 1969, *149*, 68–79.

Johnson, L.C. A psychophysiology for all states. *Psychophysiology*, 1970, *6*, 501–516.

Levy, J.L. The physiological position of rest and phoria. *American Journal of Opthamology*, 1969, *68*, 706–713.

Ornstein, R.E. *The Psychology of Consciousness*. San Francisco: W.H. Freeman & Company, 1972.

Smith, S.M., Brown, H.O., Toman, J.E.P., & Goodman, L.S. The lack of cerebral effects of D-Tubocurarine. *Anesthesiology*, 1947, *8*, 1–14.

Wolpe, J. Emotional conditioning and cognitions: A rejoinder to Davison & Valins. *Behavior Research & Therapy*, 1970, *8*, 103–104.

XII. Miscellaneous

Badri, M.B. A new technique for the systematic desensitization of pervasive anxiety and phobic reactions. *Journal of Psychology*, 1967, *65*, 201–208.

Blake, B.G. The Application of behaviour therapy to the treatment of alchoholism. *Behaviour Research & Therapy*, 1965, *3*, 75–85.

Blake, B.G. A follow-up of alcoholics treated by behaviour therapy. *Behaviour Research & Therapy*, 1967, *5*, 89–94.

Cautela, J.R. Desensitization factors in the hypnotic treatment of phobias. *Journal of Psychology*, 1966, *64*, 277–288.

Cautela, J.R. Hypnosis and behavior therapy. *Behaviour Research & Therapy*, 1966, *4*, 219–224.

Cautela, J.R. The Pavlovian basis of reciprocal inhibition therapy. *Conditional Reflex*, 1966, *1*, 293–300.

Cautela, J.R. Treatment of compulsive behavior by covert sensitization. *Psychological Record*, 1966, *16*, 33–41.

Cautela, J.R. Covert sensitization. *Psychological Reports*, 1967, *20*, 459–468.

Cooke, G. The efficacy of two desensitization procedures: An analogue study. *Behaviour Research & Therapy*, 1966, *4*, 17–24.

Emery, J.R., & Krumboltz, J.D. Standard versus individualized hierarchies in desensitization to reduce test anxiety. *Journal of Counseling Psychology*, 1967, *14*, 204–209.

Freeling, N.W., & Shemberg, K.M. The alleviation of test anxiety by systematic desensitization. *Behaviour Research & Therapy*, 1970, *8*, 293–299.

Gardner, W.J., Licklider, J.C.R., & Weisz, A.Z. Suppression of pain by sound. *Science*, 1960, *132*, 32–33.

Garfield, Z.H., Darwin, P.L., Singer, B.A., & McBrearty, J.F. Effect of "in vivo" training on experimental desensitization of a phobia. *Psychological Reports*, 1967, *20*, 515–519.

Geer, J.H., & Silverman, I. Treatment of a recurrent nightmare by behavior-modification procedures. *Journal of Abnormal Psychology*, 1967, *72*, 188–190.

Gelder, M.G., Marks, I.M., & Wolff, H.H. Desensitization and psychotherapy in the treatment of phobic states: a controlled inquiry. *British Journal of Psychiatry*, 1967, *113*, 53–73.

Graziano, A.M., & Kean, J.E. Programmed relaxation and reciprocal inhibition with psychotic children. *Proceedings of the Annual Convention of the American Psychological Association,* 1967, *2,* 253–254.

Hain, J.D., Butcher, R.H., & Stevenson, I. Systematic desensitization therapy: An analysis of results in twenty-seven patients. *British Journal of Psychiatry,* 1966, *112,* 295–307.

Hardyck, C.D., Petrinovich, L.F., & Ellsworth, D.W. Feedback of speech muscle activity during silent reading: Rapid extinction. *Science,* 1966, *154,* 1467–1468.

Haughen, G., Dixon, H., & Dickel, H. *A Therapy for anxiety and tension reactions.* New York: Macmillan, 1960.

Hoenig, J., & Reed, G.F. The objective assessment of desensitization. *British Journal of Psychiatry,* 1966, *112,* 1279–1283.

Jacobs, A., Edelman, M., & Wolpin, M. Effects of differential anxiety level and the repression-sensitization dimension in desensitization therapy. *Proceedings of the Annual Convention of the American Psychological Association,* 1971, *6,* 427–428.

Jacobson, E. *Tension control for businessmen.* New York: McGraw-Hill, 1963.

Jacobson, E. *Biology of emotions: New understanding derived from biological. multidisciplinary investigation; first electrophysiological measurements.* Springfield, Ill.: C.C. Thomas, 1967.

Jacobson, E. (Ed.). *Tension in Medicine.* Springfield, Ill.: C.C. Thomas, 1967.

Jameson, J.S., & Vernon, P. Variables affecting Wolpean systematic desensitization. *Canadian Psychiatric Association Journal,* 1970, *15,* 41–47.

Johnson, L.C. A psychophysiology for all states. *Psychophysiology,* 1970, *6,* 501–516.

Kahn, M., & Baker, B. Desensitization with minimal therapist contact. *Journal of Abnormal Psychology,* 1968, *73,* 198–200.

Katahn, M. Systematic desensitization and counseling for anxiety in a college basketball player. *Journal of Special Education,* 1967, *1,* 309–314.

Kraft, T. Behaviour therapy and the treatment of sexual perversions. *Psychotherapy and psychosomatics,* 1967, *15,* 351–357.

Kraft, T., & Al-Issa, I. Behavior therapy and the treatment of frigidity. *American Journal of Psychotherapy,* 1967, *21,* 116–120.

Lader, M.H., Gelder, M.G., & Marks, I.M. Palmar skin conductance measures as predictors of response to desensitization. *Journal of Psychosomatic Research,* 1967, *11,* 283–290.

Lader, M.H., & Mathews, A.M. A physiological model of phobic anxiety and desensitization. *Behaviour Research & Therapy,* 1968, *6,* 411–421.

Lang, P.J. The mechanics of desensitization and the laboratory study of human fear. In C.M. Franks (Ed.), *Behavior Therapy: Appraisal and Status.* New York: McGraw-Hill, 1969, pp. 160–191.

Lang, P.J., Melamed, B.G., & Hart, J. A psychophysiological analysis of fear modification using an automated desensitization procedure. *Journal of Abnormal Psychology,* 1970, *76,* 220–234.

Lazarus, A.A. Variations in desensitization therapy. *Psychotherapy: Theory, Research and Practice,* 1968, *5,* 50–52.

London, P., & McDevitt, R.A. Effects of hypnotic susceptibility and training on responses to stress. *Journal of Abnormal Psychology,* 1970, *76,* 336–348.

Marks, I.M., Gelder, M.G., & Edwards, G. Hypnosis and desensitization for phobias: A controlled prospective trial. *British Journal of Psychiatry,* 1968, *114,* 1263–1274.

Migler, B., & Wople, J. Automated self-desensitization: A case report. *Behaviour Research & Therapy,* 1967, *5,* 133–135.

Neki, J.S. Yoga and psychoanalysis. *Comprehensive Psychiatry,* 1967, *8,* 160–167.

Paben, M., & Rosentswieg, J. Control of muscular tension in learning a novel gross motor skill. *Perceptual and Motor Skills,* 1971, *32,* 556–558.

Paul, G.L. Insight versus desensitization in psychotherapy two years after termination. *Journal of Consulting Psychology,* 1967, *31,* 333–348.

Paul, G.L. Two-year follow-up of systematic desensitization in therapy groups. *Journal of Abnormal Psychology,* 1968, *73,* 119–130.

Paul, G.L., & Shannon, D.T. Treatment of anxiety through systematic desensitization in therapy groups. *Journal of Abnormal Psychology,* 1966, *71,* 124–135.

Rachman, S. The treatment of anxiety and phobic reactions by systematic desensitization psychotherapy. *Journal of Abnormal and Social Psychology,* 1959, *58,* 259–263.

Rachman, S. Studies in desensitization: II. Flooding. *Behaviour Research & Therapy,* 1966, *4,* 1–6.

Rachman, S. Studies in desensitization: III. Speed of generalization. *Behaviour Research & Therapy,* 1966, *4,* 7–15.

Rachman, S. *Phobias: Their nature and control.* Springfield, Ill.: C.C. Thomas, 1968.

Ramsay, R.W., Barends, J., Breuker, J. & Kruseman A. Massed versus spaced desensitization of fear. *Behaviour Research & Therapy,* 1966, *4,* 205–207.

Rifkin, B.G. The treatment of cardiac neurosis using systematic desensitization. *Behaviour Research & Therapy,* 1968, *6,* 239–241.

Ritter, B. The group desensitization of children's snake phobias using vicarious and contact desensitization procedures. *Behaviour Research & Therapy*, 1968, *6*, 1–6.

Silverman, I.E. & Geer, J. The elimination of a recurrent nightmare by desensitization of a related probia. *Behaviour Research & Therapy*, 1968, *6*, 109–111.

Suinn, R.M. The desensitization of test-anxiety by group and individual treatment. *Behaviour Research & Therapy*, 1968, *6*, 385–387.

Todd, F.J., & Kelly, R. J. The use of hypnosis to facilitate conditioned relaxation responses: A report of three cases. *Journal of Behavior Therapy & Experimental Psychiatry*, 1970, *1*, 295–298.

Valins, S., & Ray, A.A. Effects of cognitive desensitization on avoidance behavior. *Journal of Personality and Social Psychology*, 1967, *7*, 345–350.

Wagner, M.K., & Cauthen, N.R. A comparison of reciprocal inhibition and operant conditioning in the systematic desensitization of a fear of snakes. *Behaviour Research & Therapy*, 1968, *6*, 225–227.

Weitzman, B. Behavior therapy and psychotherapy. *Psychological Review*, 1967, *74*, 300–317.

Wells, W.P. Relaxational-rehearsal: A variant of systematic desensitization. *Psychotherapy: Therapy, Research & Practice*, 1970, *7*, 224–225.

White, J.G., Caldbeck-Meenan, J., & McAllister, H. The desensitization of phobic anxiety and its physiological concomitants. *Papers in Psychology*, 1968, *2*, 1–7.

Wilson, G.D. Efficacy of "flooding" procedures in desensitization of fear: A theoretical note. *Behaviour Research and Therapy*, 1967, *5*, 138.

Wolpe, J. For phobia: A hair of the hound. *Psychology Today*, 1969 (June), *3*, 34–37.

Wolpe, J., Lazarus, A.A., & Fried, R. Psychophysiological correlates of systematic desensitization of phobias: Preliminary findings. *Conditional Reflex*, 1968, *3*, 139.

Wolpin, M., & Raines, J. Visual imagery, expected roles and extinction as possible factors in reducing fear and avoidance behavior. *Behaviour Research & Therapy*, 1966, *4*, 25–37.

ADDITIONAL RELAXATION RESOURCES

What you've just experienced is only a small part of what is is available to help you relax. Remember that the goal in all this is to develop your own inner resources for relaxation. But until you've developed sufficient independence and self-reliance, an outside resource can be extremely useful. We all have to start somewhere, whether it's an instruction manual, a mechanical device or a course. Here are some resources whose level of application varies widely. All are of value, however, and can be helpful to some, if not all.

Free Booklet
Public Relations Dept.
Blue Cross and Blue Shield of Maryland
700 East Joppa Road
Baltimore MD 21204
A free 96-page booklet entitled *Stress* by Dr. Donald Oken

Tapes
Cognetics, Inc.
P.O. Box 592
Saratoga CA 95070

Big Sur Recordings
2015 Bridgeway
Sausalito CA 94965

Both offer a wide selection of topics in humanistic and transpersonal psychology, including structural integration, breathing therapy, martial arts and body psychotherapies. Write for the catalogs (Big Sur's costs 50¢).
Dr. William R. Parker
1807 Westcliff Drive
Newport Beach CA 92660
Offers "Relaxation/Meditation," a Christian meditation.

Electronic Sound Conditioner
Edmund Scientific Co.
300 Edscorp Building
Barrington NJ 08007
The ESC comes in two versions. One simulates four kinds of soothing sounds of ocean surf and rain ($79.95 postpaid). The other produces "white sound" of no specific tone to help mask unwanted noise ($28.00). Company claims ESC aids relaxation and sleep. Write for descriptive literature.

Course for Professionals
   Nyingma Institute
   1815 Highland Place
   Berkeley CA 94709
   Nyingma Institute, a center for Tibetan Buddhism in
   America, offers the Kum Nye training workshop for psychotherapists, physiotherapists and other health professionals. The Nyingma system of physical exercises, postures,
   breathing techniques and massage helps to release block-
   ages so that body sensations and mental attitudes become
   flexible and open. Write for the catalog.

Massage
   This is powerful means of producing relaxation. There are
   books and courses widely available. *The Massage Book* by
   George Downing (Randon House/Bookworks, 1972) is
   useful. So are legitimate massage parlors. You'll be surprised at the variety of cultural approaches to massage—
   Swedism, Japanese, Sufi, polarity, etc.

Sex Therapy
   Enormous tension is caused by sexual disfunction and poor
   sexual relationships. There are dozens of books intended
   to relax your ideas about your own sexual limits or interests. Two of the best are *The Joy of Sex* and its sequel,
   More Joy of Sex; both are edited by Alex Comfort and
   are available from Simon and Schuster.

Physical Exercise
   Check with your YMCA or its equivalent to see what
   courses of instruction it offers.

Meditation
   There are many meditation systems. The best-known is
   Transcendental Meditation (TM®), with hundreds of cen-
   ters around the country where you can get instruction.
   Look in your telephone directory under Students Inter-
   national Meditation Society or write for information to
   national headquarters:
   SIMS
   1015 Gayley Ave.
   Los Angeles CA 90028
   Home correspondence courses are also available. One of
   the best is available from:
   University of the Trees
   Box 644
   Boulder Creek CA 95006

Two useful books on meditation are *How to Meditate* by
Lawrence LeShan (Bantam, 1974) and *What Is Medita-
tion?* edited by John White (Doubleday-Anchor, 1974).
The latter lists further resources on meditation.

The Phenix Society is a national friendship society devoted to life-enrichment through reading, discussion and
meditation. Local chapters give instruction in meditation.
The Wisdom College, sponsored by the Society, is a four-
year correspondence course in consciousness expansion
and planetary management. For information about the
Society and the Wisdom College, write to:

The Phenix Society
Box 25
Guilford CT 06437

Spiritual Systems and Schools

Having a method for eliciting the relaxation response is
not in itself sufficient to *eliminate* stress and tension from
your life. A method can help you control these health-
wreckers, but to eliminate them you need something more:
character development and value refinement. This matter
is uniformly ignored in the literature on relaxation.

Stress, tension, anxiety and nervousness originate in the
ego. But the ego is an illusion, only a false image in your
mind. It is this mental state of egotism that produces most
discomfort, pain and suffering. If you want to root these
out at the source, remember what we said in Section III
about the origin of most techniques for relaxation. They
are modern adaptions of the beginning steps in some of
the world's great spiritual systems.

Those systems recognize clearly the nature of ego and
have developed procedures for going far beyond mere tension reduction. It is no accident that society's models of the
fully-developed human, the self-actualized person, include
many saints and holy people. They have been revered for
many reasons: their compassion, devotion, inspirational
words of wisdom, service to the world. But the trait that
is of particular importance for us here is their equanimity,
their tranquility, their ease of mind and peace of heart in
the face of circumstances that for most others would be
extremely stressful, if not overwhelming.

What has been their secret? Each of them, in his own
way arising from his particular tradition, has discovered
the truth of the saying, "Let go and let God." When a
sense of the infinite or the transpersonal replaces our
usual narrow self-centeredness, there is no longer a mental
basis for fear, anger, tension. Instead, the perfectly har-
monious functioning of the cosmos operates through us

—and the cosmos is always balanced, at peace with itself.

We therefore suggest—in closing this book on how to feel better, reduce stress and overcome tension—that you begin to investigate the deeper roots of religious and spiritual traditions. The essence of those traditions is not a moralizing exhortation to be a better person, but rather a method by which you can personally experience a deepening of wisdom and a growth of character through the elimination of ego. In the process you can gain all the benefits described here, while reducing your personal contribution to humanity's distress.

There are many systems, schools, groups, organizations and paths that help people grow in spiritual awareness to a higher and healthier state of being. Three books that give a wide listing of them by name, location and psychospiritual orientation are *The Highest State of Consciousness* edited by John White (Doubleday-Anchor, 1972), *Spiritual Community Guide* (Spiritual Community Publications, Box 1080, San Rafael CA 94902, 1974) and *Awakening: Ways to Psycho-Spiritual Growth* by C. William Henderson (Prentice-Hall, 1975). All are available in paperback editions from bookstores. Other places to find access are advertisements and directories in the monthly national *East West Journal* and *New Age Journal,* both widely available in metaphysically-oriented bookstores and health food stores. Major city newspapers often carry ads and directories; *The Village Voice* is especially rich in offerings. College newspapers and bulletin boards are other easy ways to gain access to the spiritual community.

ABOUT THE EDITORS

JOHN WHITE is an author, editor and teacher engaged in the exploration of consciousness. From 1972-74 he was director of education for The Institute of Noetic Sciences. He has taught in high school and college. He is a member of the board of directors of The Phenix Society, a national association of men and women who seek to improve the quality of their lives through reading, discussion and meditation.

Mr. White is editor of *The Highest State of Consciousness, What Is Meditation?, Frontiers of Consciousness, Other Worlds, Other Universes* (co-edited with Brad Steiger) and *Psychic Exploration.* He recently wrote *Everything You Want to Know About TM®.* His writing has appeared in many popular and professional journals, including *Reader's Digest* and *Saturday Review.* He is an editor of *Psychic* and *Human Dimensions* magazines, and is on the editorial board of *Journal of Altered States of Consciousness.*

Mr. White lives in Cheshire, Connecticut with his wife Barbara and their four children.

JAMES FADIMAN, Ph.D., is the director of The Institute of Noetic Sciences in Menlo Park, California. He is the director and past president of the Association for Transpersonal Psychology. He has taught at Brandeis University, California State University at San Francisco, and Stanford University.

Dr. Fadiman is on the editorial boards of several journals, has edited *The Proper Study of Man* and co-edited *Exploring Madness.* He is co-author of *Personality and Personal Growth* with Robert Frager. He has also lectured and led workshops internationally. Most recently he has become involved with the movement for Integral Medicine, and has spoken at medical conferences and on national television about it.

Dr. Fadiman lives in Menlo Park, California with his wife Dorothy and their two children, Renee and Maria.